HEALTH EDUCATION AUTHORITY

Catering for healthy eating in schools

Anne Coles
Sheila Turner

A report prepared for the Health Education Authority by Anne Coles and Sheila Turner of the Institute of Education, University of London

Published in 1993

Health Education Authority
Hamilton House
Mabledon Place
LONDON WC1H 9TX

ISBN 1 85448 488 5

Front cover photograph by Sheila Halsall, © Barnabys Picture Library
Typeset by Witwell Ltd, Southport
Printed in Great Britain by The Cromwell Press, Melksham, Wilts.

Catering
for healthy
eating in

4 Week Loan

This book is due for return on or before the last date shown
below

University of Cumbria
24/7 renewals Tel:0845 602 6124

CONTENTS

EXECUTIVE SUMMARY

In January 1992 the Health Education Authority (HEA) commissioned a review of steps taken by Local Authorities (LAs) to encourage healthy eating in schools. The research was undertaken by Dr Anne Coles and Dr Sheila Turner, Institute of Education, University of London between January 13th and April 10th 1992.

The project had two aims.

- To review and report on the effect and use of contract specifications on nutritional standards for school meals in England, so identifying 'good practice'.
- To explore ways in which the HEA might provide information and guidance to both clients and contractors to help them improve the nutritional standards of school meals.

The research relied on two methods. Questionnaires were sent to all 109 Directors of Education in England and were followed by in-depth discussions and visits to selected boroughs, metropolitan authorities and counties. The following topics were addressed.

- The type of school meals service provided.
- The extent and nature of the nutritional specifications in the contract for school meals services.
- The extent to which healthy eating policies were pursued.
- Successful initiatives that LAs had taken to foster healthy eating in schools.
- Ideas that LAs had about ways in which the HEA could help them to improve the nutritional standards of school meal provision.
- Concerns about the future of the service including anticipated effects of Local Management of Schools (LMS).

The response rate to the questionnaire was high at 87% and therefore the study provides a comprehensive picture of the school meals service during the time when the survey was undertaken.

Analysis of the results from the survey indicate that:

- The great majority (94%) of school meals contracts are run by Direct Services Organisations.
- A small minority (11%) of LAs make only statutory provision for school meals.
- The majority (98%) of LAs have specifications for healthy eating

in their contracts, but the nature and detail of these specifications vary.

- All LAs have monitoring procedures, but there is considerable variation in the way in which monitoring is undertaken and the extent to which nutritional specifications are monitored.
- Some LAs have difficulty ensuring that contract specifications are monitored adequately.
- Some LAs have difficulty ensuring that contract specifications, policies and guidelines on healthy eating are met.

Ideas for ways in which the HEA could help support and promote the school meals service were made by clients, caterers and teachers and include the following.

- Provision of specific information and/or advice about meeting appropriate nutritional standards in meals.
- Support for school meals campaigns at national and local level.
- Support in overcoming perceived financial constraints.
- Reinstating nutritional guidelines for school meals.
- Support for nutrition education in schools and in the home.

A number of issues, which the authors hope will inform future discussion about the school meals service, are identified in Chapter 7 and can be summarised as follows.

- Defining and implementing nutritional standards for school meals needs to be realistic and to acknowledge the constraints and complexity of the present system.
- School meal provision should be seen in the context of the school as a whole.
- Long term strategies for change should be developed and implemented in stages.
- Short term and pilot promotions appear to have limited value in changing children's eating habits.

Anne Coles
Sheila Turner
Institute of Education
University of London

ACKNOWLEDGEMENTS

We thank all those who supported us in this research project including Directors of Education, clients and caterers in the school meals service, cook supervisors, head teachers and pupils, all of whom gave unstintingly of their time. We are most grateful to those individuals, organisations and projects we contacted during the course of our research for providing information and for answering our queries. Regrettably we cannot mention by name all those who gave us help and advice.

In particular we thank the Health Education Authority for their help in supporting the project, especially the Project Director, Rosemary Hunt. We also acknowledge the help provided by the original background paper which was prepared for the Health Education Authority by Isobel Cole-Hamilton. We are particularly appreciative of the advice we received from Jenny Poulter, who acted as consultant to the project, and who provided cogent and sound advice. We are most grateful for the invaluable practical help given by Dr Ann Abel, Gillie Bonner and Sandra Carey during the research and in the preparation of the final report – and for their patience and good humour in dealing with our, at times, unrealistic expectations. We also thank Liz Purcell for her help in preparing the report for publication.

ABBREVIATIONS USED IN THE REPORT

AMMA	Assistant Masters and Mistresses Association
BDA	British Dietetic Association
CCT	Compulsory Competitive Tendering
COMA	Committee on Medical Aspects of Food Policy
CPG	The Coronary Prevention Group
DES	Department of Education and Science (now Department for Education)
DFE	Department for Education
DoH	Department of Health
DHSS	Department of Health and Social Security
DRV	Dietary Reference Value
DSO	Direct Service Organisations
HEA	Health Education Authority
ILEA	Inner London Education Authority
LA	Local Authority
LACA	Local Authority Caterers Association
LEA	Local Education Authority
LGMB	Local Government Management Board
LMS	Local Management of Schools
NACNE	National Advisory Committee on Nutrition Education
RDA	Recommended Daily Allowance
WHO	World Health Organisation

1 INTRODUCTION

Since 1989 there have been major changes in Local Authority (LA) services. These have included some that have had a major impact on schools and the school meals service.

- The Education Act (1988) introduced Local Management of Schools (LMS), with schools taking responsibility for managing their own budgets, and the introduction of the National Curriculum in schools in England and Wales.
- The Local Government Act (1989) introduced Compulsory Competitive Tendering (CCT) for Local Authority (LA) services, including school meals.

These changes provide the context for this review of steps taken by Local Education Authorities (LEAs) to encourage healthy eating in schools.

There have been several reports that have drawn attention to the consumption of particular food items by young people.

The report on the diets of British schoolchildren (Department of Health, 1989) provided information about the food that 10–11-year-old and 14–15-year-old children were eating, including the quantities of fatty foods, biscuits, cakes and soft drinks. This report highlighted the amount of chips, buns and pastries eaten as part of school meals.

Concerns about the intakes of specific nutrients, for example fat, are reflected in other reports, including that by the World Health Organisation (WHO) (1990). Reports such as these indicate the importance of school catering in the diets of young people, but there is little information about the impact of these reports on catering in schools in England.

Studies of the diets of schoolchildren raise important issues, in particular:

- the importance of school meals in contributing to optimum nutrition for growth and health;
- education about food and health can be reinforced, or undermined, by the choices available in school canteens.

Preliminary discussions by the Health Education Authority (HEA) with a range of organisations and agencies indicated that a survey of the steps being taken by LAs to encourage healthy eating as part of catering in schools would be timely, valuable and appropriate.

PURPOSE OF THE RESEARCH

The HEA identified two aims for the research project.

- To review and report on the effect and use of contract specifications on nutritional standards for school meals in England, so identifying 'good practice'.
- To explore ways in which the HEA might provide information and guidance to both clients and contractors to help them improve the nutritional standards of school meals.

ORGANISATION OF THE SURVEY

The HEA envisaged the survey, which was commissioned in mid-January 1992, in three phases.

- **Phase 1** A review of the extent and nature of nutritional specifications used by LEAs in contracts for school meals using a questionnaire sent to all Directors of Education in England.
- **Phase 2** A detailed investigation (including in-depth interviews) of the nature of LEA nutrition specifications, monitoring procedures, the nature of the contract, and the specific needs of the LEA in taking these specifications forward.
- **Phase 3** This phase, which could be developed depending upon the outcomes of phases 1 and 2, would identify contractors who are successfully meeting nutritional specifications and establish the reasons for success, problems in meeting nutritional specifications, and support needed by contractors.

2 REVIEW OF THE POSITION REGARDING SCHOOL MEALS

'. . . a quick, cheap and easy way of improving and protecting the health of children . . .' (Fisher, 1987)

School meals have long been viewed as important for social, nutritional and educational reasons.

Concerns about the health and welfare of children, particularly the poor, formed the focus of the original pressures for the introduction of school meals a century ago, and are still prevalent. The importance of school meals at the present time has been highlighted by the School Meals Campaign (1992) and White, Cole-Hamilton & Dibb (1992). It is therefore important to consider the history of school meals provision before looking in more detail at current provision.

HISTORICAL PERSPECTIVE

The origins of the present provision of school meals in England can be traced to the Education (Provision of Meals) Act of 1906 which gave LAs powers to provide meals for 'Children attending an elementary school within their area . . . unable by reason of lack of food to take advantage of the education provided for them' (Education Act, 1906).

Despite the powers given to LAs by the 1906 Education Act, the provision of school meals for many years was limited to a small proportion of children in elementary schools, namely those in greatest need.

By 1939, school meals were provided by approximately half of LAs. National provision of school meals for the majority of children was an outcome of wartime legislation when meals, based on minimum nutritional requirements, were provided free to eligible children and at cost price to others.

One of the outcomes of wartime rationing and the extension of school meals and milk provision from 1939 to 1945, was the improved nutritional status of children. The report by the Chief Medical Officer on public health from 1939 to 1945 (Ministry of Health, 1945), provided evidence from clinical surveys that children were healthier than they had been before the outbreak of war and that their death from disease was low.

After the war school meals continued on a national basis and were associated with the development of the Welfare State and the implementation of the influential Education Act of 1944.

The Education Act of 1944 (Section 49) made LEAs responsible for providing milk and school meals for pupils at schools maintained by them. Enshrined in the Act was the idea that school meals should be part of the school day, rather than merely an adjunct to the curriculum.

Nutritional standards

Although the educational ideals underpinning the provision of school meals largely disappeared between 1960 and 1990, the nutritional standards governing school meals continued to be controlled by the Department of Education and Science (DES) until the Education Act of 1980.

As late as 1975 the Working Party on the Nutritional Aspects of School Meals (DES, 1975) recommended that school meals should continue to provide 880 kilocalories (one-third of the recommended daily intake) and 29 grams of protein. Guidelines were also given for the provision of fresh meat and the inclusion of milk and cheese. The inclusion of milk as part of meals was stressed because, as the working party pointed out, school milk was no longer provided for the majority of older pupils in junior schools. Concern was expressed about the snacks available, particularly confectionery and soft drinks, which could lead to dental caries.

The Education Act (1980) was particularly controversial as it moved the responsibility for nutritional standards for school meals to LEAs. The social services element of school meals provision continued for children deemed to be 'in need', for example, children of parents on low incomes. The meals provided for these children were the same as for other children in the school. The devolved responsibility for school meals provision was less cause for concern than the fact that LEAs were no longer required to meet nutritional standards for meals or to provide a 'set meal' for pupils.

Concerns about the lack of nutritional standards and the effect of these on children, particularly those entitled to free school meals, led to pressure on the Department of Education and Science (now the Department for Education) to reintroduce nutritional standards for school meals.

In 1982 the report by the Education, Science and Arts Committee (1982) on school meals, recommended a return to nutritional standards for school meals. The recommendation was rejected by the DES with the reported comment that there was no guarantee that pupils would eat the food prescribed! (Spencer, 1982). This comment reflected one of the concerns in the years up to 1980 concerning wastage.

After 1980, as suggested by the Assistant Masters and Mistresses Association and the Coronary Prevention Group (AMMA/CPG, 1987), problems arose because LEAs did not necessarily make their school meals caterers aware of the objectives of the service or require them to meet a common nutritional standard. The pattern of provision also changed as more secondary and many middle schools moved to a cafeteria service, though few primary schools followed.

The move to different types of provision in itself is not necessarily a cause for concern, but the lack of control over nutritional standards, particularly in the context of the diets of needy children, has been viewed as problematic.

Organisations such as the Coronary Prevention Group (AMMA/ CPG, 1987) have continued to press for a more coherent policy for school meals provision, to reflect nutritional recommendations by national committees. These include NACNE (National Advisory Committee on Nutrition Education, 1983) and COMA (Committee on Medical Aspects of Food Policy, 1984) and international organisations such as the WHO (1990).

Eating patterns

Current provision of school meals has to be viewed in the wider context of changes in eating patterns in the population as a whole, and changing views about diet and health.

Surveys of the diets of schoolchildren, including the national survey by the Department of Health reported in 1986 (Wenlock *et al.*, 1986; Department of Health, 1989), have revealed major shifts in eating patterns amongst children. The Department of Health (DoH) survey findings show that chips, buns and pastries dominate the weekday lunches of schoolchildren. Chips eaten as part of a school meal accounted for 50% of the daily weekday consumption of chips among older pupils.

School meals are only one element in the diet of children, but the national survey findings that three-quarters of children in the survey had fat intakes contributing more than the 35% of energy levels recommended by COMA (1984) indicate that school meals policy and provision should be reviewed and monitored on a regular basis.

NUTRITIONAL GUIDELINES FOR SCHOOL MEALS SINCE 1980

Since 1980 there have been efforts to reintroduce appropriate nutritional guidelines for school meals. However, only one set of recommended nutritional standards has been suggested, though there have been minor variations to it. These standards were originally developed by community dietitians in the wake of NACNE and were adopted by the British Dietetic Association (BDA) and the CPG and then used by the London Food Commission. The same standards formed the basis of Tony Banks's unsuccessful private member's bill in 1987 which aimed to reintroduce compulsory nutritional standards for school meals. They were also the basis for the former ILEA guidelines, though these were never formally authorised (Maggie Sanderson, personal communication).

The standards were based partly on NACNE guidelines and also on an examination of the data presented in *The Diets of British School Children* (DoH, 1989) which showed the contribution of the school meal to children's dietary intakes. The standards are shown in Table 1.

Table 1 Nutritional standards

Nutrient	Recommended amount in school meal
Energy	Not less than 30% of the recommended daily allowance (RDA)
Fat	33–35% of energy (approximately 32 g per meal)
Sugar	No more than 10% energy per school meal (i.e. no more than 25 g of added sugar to the meal)
Fibre	30% of the daily fibre intake, which is equal to approximately 8 g
Iron	Not less than 35–40% of the RDA
Protein and carbohydrate	No specific recommendations have been made. The authors would concur with NACNE that 11% of total energy should be derived from protein. Therefore 54% of total energy would be provided from carbohydrate
Vitamin A	Not less than 35% of the RDA
Vitamin C	Not less than 50% of the RDA
Vitamin D	Vitamin D-rich foods should be used where appropriate

Source: AMMA/CPG (1987)

3 SURVEY METHODOLOGY

The timetable for the survey is shown in Appendix 2. The study began in mid-January with the development and trialling of questionnaires. Questionnaires were then sent to Directors of Education in the remaining LEAs in England.

During Phase 2 of the research, visits were made to 12 selected boroughs, metropolitan authorities and counties. Formal and informal interviews were also carried out by telephone. The research was completed by mid-April 1992.

PRELIMINARY ACTIVITIES

The questionnaire was designed by the researchers, in consultation with the HEA. In addition, nine experts were asked to comment on the draft questionnaire. The questionnaire was piloted in twelve LEAs selected by means of a random structured sample.

The main lessons learnt from the pilot were as follows.

- There was a real problem in ensuring that questionnaires reached the right people. Sometimes the documents addressed to the Director of Education reached neither him or her, nor the PA. Personal follow-up by phone was frequently necessary.
- It clearly took time for officers to fill in questionnaires, even when the information was readily available as we were assured. Our impression was that client services officers were often out of their offices for much of the day, most days of the week. Because of the likely delays in receiving completed questionnaires, it was decided to go ahead with field visits to LEAs before the questionnaires were analysed. Otherwise the research would not have been completed in the spring term.
- The respondents appreciated the lemon-coloured pilot version of the questionnaire, which was easy to see on a crowded desk. Bright gold paper was therefore used for the questionnaire.
- Several of the officers to whom we spoke on the phone were forthcoming and keen to talk about what their LEA was doing to promote healthy eating. We were encouraged to think there would be no difficulty in talking to most people again over the phone when we wanted to carry out in-depth interviews. Similarly we felt that there would be no undue difficulty in visiting LEAs with good practices, as suggested in the project proposal.

THE QUESTIONNAIRE

The questionnaire (see Appendix 1) had sections addressing the following issues.

- Overview of the school meals service.
- Contract specifications concerned with healthy eating and nutrition.
- Healthy eating policies or guidelines.
- Local Management of Schools and its effects on the school meals service.
- Ways in which the HEA could help LEAs develop the nutritional standards of school meals.
- Successful initiatives that LEAs had taken to foster healthy eating in schools.

The questions asked were the same as those used in the pilot. The first page provided an introduction to the questionnaire.

First section

The first section of the questionnaire asked for factual information to give an overview of the school meals service in each LEA. This information was needed to set the answers to the main part of the questionnaire in a proper context. It also provided variables directly comparable to those collected routinely by bodies such as the DFE and the Local Government Management Board (LGMB - see Note 1, page 57). Furthermore, the characteristics of LEAs responding to the survey could be compared with the characteristics of non-responding LEAs, to identify respondent bias.

The other sections

The other sections dealt with four topics of particular concern to the HEA.

- The extent and nature of nutritional specifications in the school meals contract, and/or the extent to which healthy eating policies were nonetheless pursued.
- The effect, or likely effect of LMS on the provision of school meals.
- The identification of ways in which the HEA could help LEAs to improve the nutritional standards of the school meals service.
- Successful initiatives that LEAs had taken to foster healthy eating in school catering.

Answering the questionnaire

As some of the questions could be politically sensitive it was made clear in a covering letter that 'difficult' questions could be left unanswered. Several respondents did leave certain questions blank, noting that the information was confidential.

As the person delegated to answer the questionnaire might not have access to all the necessary information, it was suggested in the introduction to the questionnaire that the informant might wish to consult colleagues. It was clear during follow-up that the questionnaire was sometimes passed around, either between several council officers or between the client officer and the Direct Service Organisation (DSO) caterer.

One of the constraints on the questionnaire was the need for brevity. Previous surveys, for example, Local Authority Caterers Association (1991) have had low response rates and it was felt that a long document would be a deterrent. This meant that it was impossible to explore some of the more complex topics as fully as desired, particularly concerning healthy eating specifications and monitoring. These subjects were therefore explored at greater depth during face-to-face and telephone interviews.

Providing contract specifications

Respondents were asked to provide copies of contract specifications related to healthy eating. Of those stating that they had such specifications 64% sent photocopied extracts. Some people may not have provided specifications because of the bulk of the specification documents. Sometimes they run into several hundred pages, including not only details of ingredients, but also portion sizes, recipes to be used, meal characteristics and menu cycles. Since healthy eating principles might apply to all these areas it could be difficult to decide what to send. In other cases it is probable that specifications were regarded as confidential.

THE QUALITATIVE RESEARCH

Visits were made to 12 LEAs which were selected because:

* verbal recommendations of interesting initiatives had been received from at least two sources;
* they provided appropriate socio-economic and geographical coverage.

Three were London Boroughs, four were Metropolitan Districts and five were Non-Metropolitan Counties.*

All the LEAs approached agreed to a visit, but one later had to postpone it until after the end of the research because of pressure of work. Another LEA, of appropriate character, was substituted.

Visits to LEAs

During visits, in-depth interviews were held with both client and catering officers. Sometimes interviews took the form of group discussions, the precise arrangements for the talks being left to the LEAs.

Visits were made to primary and secondary schools during the mid-day meal break. This provided an opportunity to observe the school

*In 1991 the 33 London Boroughs had 372,941 pupils, the 36 Metropolitan Districts had 1,722,525 pupils and the 40 Non-Metropolitan Counties had 5,757,166 pupils.

meal. The choice of schools was left to the LEA hosts, who also attended the visit. Despite possible bias in the selection of schools, observations made on the visits were extremely useful.

Telephone interviews

Both informal and formal interviews were also carried out by telephone.

Informal interviews occurred:

- when LEAs wanted additional information before deciding whether to take part in the survey;
- when questionnaires were returned and there was a need to clarify or follow up certain points;
- when school meals' officers rang to provide additional information.

Some of these informal interviews took over an hour and dealt with far more than the original topic prompting the call.

The formal interviews were of two kinds:

- either with all LEAs for whom responsibility for providing school meals had been reduced to statutory provision only. The present provision of meals in these authorities varies considerably from authority to authority and from school to school. It would therefore have been difficult to gain an accurate impression of this group of LEAs from the questionnaires and, perhaps, a single field visit.
- or with a sample of LEAs who had not sent copies of healthy eating specifications to see whether their contracts were very different in this respect from those who had sent us information.

During these formal interviews other topics, which seemed important on the basis of the questionnaire responses, were explored in a little more depth.

Recording results

Interview schedules were used for in-depth interviews and group discussions, with checklists for the participant observation in schools. Brief notes were made during visits with field reports completed the same day. The researchers made the first two visits together to reduce inter-interviewer differences.

4 RESULTS

The questionnaire was answered by 94 of the 109 LEAs in England, but one response was received too late for analysis. If the City of London, which has only one maintained school, is discounted, this gives a response rate of 87%. Of the 14 non-respondents, only 2 refused. Several questionnaires are 'still being completed'! Six of the 33 London Boroughs, 4 of the 36 Metropolitan Districts and 4 of the 40 Non-Metropolitan Counties did not reply, giving response rates of 82%, 89% and 90% respectively. A preliminary examination of the 1990 DES figures on school meals suggested no particular differences between respondents and non-respondents.

Most questionnaires (71%) were answered by the client service officers to whom they were addressed. Some (20%) were answered by officers who were in the Education Department, but who could not be clearly identified as being in client services sections. Caterers (8%) answered and, in one case, a catering consultant completed the questionnaire. The character of the caterers' responses has been compared with those of the others and commented upon where necessary.

The view that it was important for data collection to be confined to the spring term, was confirmed by the research. Several LEAs wrote in their questionnaires that meal prices would rise in the summer term. A few other LEAs reported that there would be changes in their contracts in April 1992. In interviews, caterers in particular commented spontaneously on the way school meal numbers declined in the summer term.

A comparatively small proportion of the LEAs reported difficulty implementing nutritional specifications, policies or guidelines. Officers may have been reluctant to admit difficulties. Alternatively, they may have been reluctant to answer the open-ended question that followed if they did state that they had problems.

A few open-ended questions were poorly answered. Comparatively few respondents answered a question on how the HEA could help LEAs to promote healthy eating in schools, which was asked partly as a means of giving the questionnaire a positive image and partly because we hoped that the answers would guide us when we came to explore the topic at greater depth in interviews. This low response rate was probably partly because the answer required some thought.

Discussion of the results in the following sections concerns only those LEAs that responded to the questionnaire.

CHARACTERISTICS OF THE SCHOOL MEALS SERVICE

Who runs it?

In almost all LEAs the school meals service is run by the DSOs who ran it before CCT. In 5 cases, the service is run by private caterers, and in one other the contracts are divided between the DSO and a private firm. In 9 LEAs, where there is only a statutory meal service, the DSO has a much reduced role, usually as the provider of a packed sandwich lunch, and many schools make individual arrangements with private caterers to provide meals.

Table 2 Date when the present contracts began
Where there were several contracts with staggered dates, the date given is that for the first contract.
(n=93, missing values=2)

Date		Number of LEAs (total respondents 91)
Before 1989		4
1989	Summer term	3
	Autumn term	18
1990	Spring term	9
	Summer term	2
	Autumn term	16
1991	Spring term	14
	Summer term	3
	Autumn term	12
1992	Spring term	7
	Summer term	2
	Autumn term	1

Compulsory competitive tendering

Compulsory competitive tendering (CCT) has been introduced over a period of four years. The first groups of LEAs were required to go out to tender by 1 August 1989; the last by 1 January 1992. Three LEAs have contracts with private caterers dating back to the 1980s and these contracts have not had to go through the CCT process. Some LEAs put contracts out to tender ahead of the official timetable (Local Government Management Board, 1991) (Table 2). In a few cases, the initial CCT contract has already had to be radically revised, usually as a result of financial cutbacks, and re-tendering has, or is about to occur.

Table 3 Number of contracts held by LEAs

Number of contracts	Number of LEAs (total=93)
1	57
2–5	17
more than 5	10
Devolved meals service	9

Just over 60% of the LEAs have only one contract. Where there are several, and almost 20% of LEAs have two to five contracts, it is usually because the LEA has split its area geographically. The service was divided into six or more contracts in 16% of LEAs (Table 3).

In almost every case, all the contracts belonging to a LEA were won by the same contractor.

Table 4 **Dates when present contracts expire**
(n=93, missing values=6)

Date	Number of LEAs (total respondents=87)
1992	6
1993	20
1994	34
1995	17
1996	9
1997	1

Most contracts come up for renewal (Table 4) either in the summer or in the Christmas holidays, and 76% are due to expire between July 1993 and September 1995. However, in some cases, LEAs reported the option to renew for a further year. Under the terms of CCT, contracts are normally for four years, with the option of renewing for a further year, or, in the case of Inner London Boroughs for a further two years (C. Hislop, personal communication).

From a practical viewpoint it should be noted that client services officers feel it takes almost a year to prepare a new contract, though second time around, experience may speed up the process.

Table 5 **Annual value of contracts**
As might be expected the values for London Boroughs were normally smaller than for Metropolitan Authorities and Counties, but this was not always the case.

Authority	Range (£m)	Mean Value (£m)	Total
London Boroughs (n=20)	0.25–9.0	3.12	62.43
Metropolitan Authorities (n=24)	2.30–17.8	5.58	133.78
Counties (n=27)	0.58–21.0	8.35	225.55
All LEAs (n=71)	0.25–21.0	5.94	421.76

Annual value of contracts

Seventy-six per cent of the responding LEAs sent information about the total value of their contracts. The smallest contract was £0.25 m

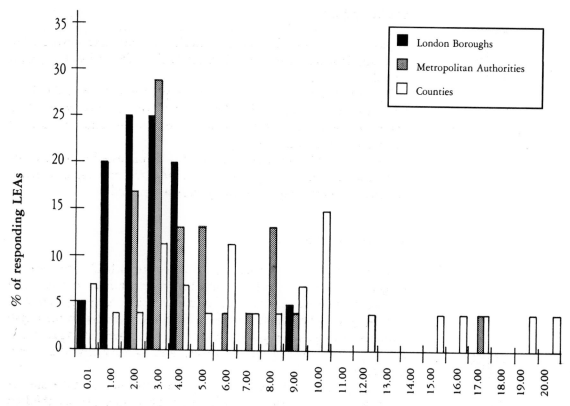

Figure 1 Annual value of contracts in £m

(in an outer London Borough) and the largest £21 m (a large non-Metropolitan County). The values of the contracts for London Boroughs, Metropolitan Authorities and Counties are shown in Table 5 and Figure 1.

The meal service

Cafeteria or set meal

In general, secondary schools have cash cafeterias (Figure 2), but there are some secondary schools with a choice of set meal in 6% of LEAs. Only one LEA had no cash cafeterias.

Cash cafeterias are far more popular with older students than traditional meals. They are generally regarded as the only viable type of food service in senior schools. Typically, they offer a wide variety of snacks and fast-food items, as well as home-cooked hot dishes, often in the form of the 'meal of the day' or 'healthy eating choice'.

Primary schools generally report having set meals, but 20% of LEAs also have schools with a cafeteria-style service. These are *not* normally cash cafeterias. Rather, they provide a limited choice of items from which the children make up a set-price meal.

Choice of food

Choice was not asked about specifically in the questionnaires, but generally it seems that choice is more likely to be available in larger schools.

Opinion is divided about whether the youngest children should be offered a choice. Some headteachers consider that infants are unable to make up their minds fast enough to permit an efficient flow of customers through the servery.

Choice at the primary level seems to have increased in the last few years and to be increasing still. One reason is the growing proportion of children preferring or requiring vegetarian food.

Statutory meal service

Where there is only a statutory meal service, school meals are no longer subsidised by the LEA, but LEAs may continue to assist with maintenance of premises or equipment, or with charges for utilities.

Most secondary schools have been able to continue with their cash cafeterias, using a variety of contractors (e.g. private catering firms, ex DSO groups, parents' cooperatives, and occasionally the DSOs themselves).

Primary schools have commonly been unable to make similar arrangements to continue their hot meal provision. Usually children have to bring sandwiches from home, with the LEA providing a packed lunch for children entitled to a free meal.

If private caterers are providing food, the LEA normally pays for 'free meal' children to receive lunch in the canteen as before.

Number of pupils eating the school meal each day

Nationally, the proportion of children eating school meals was 42% in 1991, and 29% of these were receiving free meals (DES, 1992).

There are basically two published ways of calculating the number of students using a cash cafeteria.

- For obtaining official statistics, the DFE asks each school to count the number of students buying food from the cafeteria and those having a free meal on a particular day in January each year. (The figures for January 1992 were unavailable at the time of this survey.)
- An alternative method, which caterers thought underestimated the throughput, is to divide the cafeteria's takings by the 'authorised spend' (i.e. the amount a child who has free school meals can spend daily) assuming this is what the average student spends, and adding to it the number of students taking a free meal that day.

A few LEAs estimated the proportion of children eating school meals using the second method. The inaccuracy that results is recounted by

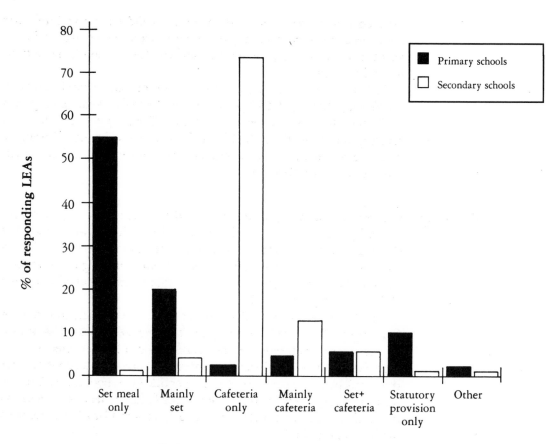

Figure 2 Type of school meal provision in primary and secondary schools

one caterer who reported that the average spend at cash cafeterias in her LEA was 55–60p, while the authorised spend was 97p. The

Table 6 Number of pupils using the school meals service each day n=93, missing values =11)

Number of pupils	Number of LEAs (total respondents=82)
5,000	0
5,000–(10,000)	5
10,000–(15,000)	14
15,000–(20,000)	22
20,000–(30,000)	12
30,000–(40,000)	10
40,000–(50,000)	6
50,000–(60,000)	3
60,000–(70,000)	3
70,000–(80,000)	3
80,000–(90,000)	2
90,000–(100,000)	1
100,000	1

difference is the result of some 'free meal' children 'topping up' their authorised spend with money from home, children buying a drink or snack to accompany a packed lunch, and children economising on their lunchtime meal.

Eighty-two LEAs answered the question on school meal numbers, estimating that 2,510,648 primary and 1,443,641 secondary pupils used the school meals service each day (Table 6). Of the 19 LEAs catering for fewer than 10,000 children, 13 were London Boroughs. Non-Metropolitan Counties generally catered for more children than the Metropolitan Districts.

Uptake of free meals

Concern has been expressed at the rather poor uptake of free school meals by those entitled to them. Data from thirty-nine authorities showed that at the primary level the mean uptake was 83% (range 53% to an improbable 100%). Data from thirty-eight authorities showed that at the secondary level the mean uptake was 62% (range 28% to an improbable 100%).

At primary level, it is relatively easy to conceal which children are in receipt of free meals; certainly most cook-supervisors do not know. At secondary level, however, such children can be identified as they pass through the till of the cash cafeteria. Some LEAs reported that there was no stigma attached to being entitled to school meals, but this may not apply everywhere. However, the failure to take up free meals to which pupils are entitled, particularly at secondary level, requires further exploration.

These figures may be compared with those in the LACA survey. Using data from 27 LEAs, the uptake figures for all pupils were 71% for London Boroughs, 77% for Counties and 80% for Metropolitan Districts (LACA, 1991).

Price of primary school meals and the authorised spend for secondary pupils entitled to a free meal

The range of prices charged for primary school meals and the authorised spend for secondary pupils entitled to a free school meal is shown in Figure 3.

In primary schools the price of a meal ranged from 45p to £1.00, the average price being 84p. In secondary schools the authorised spend ranged from 55p to £1.41, the average being 94p.

Most primary school meals costing 75p or less were in the Metropolitan Boroughs (11 out of 20). This compared with a similar situation in 6 London Boroughs and only 3 Non-Metropolitan Counties, where there were 4 LEAs charging £1.00 (Figure 3).

In primary schools the set meal is that received by children qualifying for a free lunch. In secondary schools, children entitled to a free meal receive an 'authorised spend'. The allocated amount is usually sufficient to buy 'the meal of the day', but children are free to spend the money on other items – within reason. Buying several cans

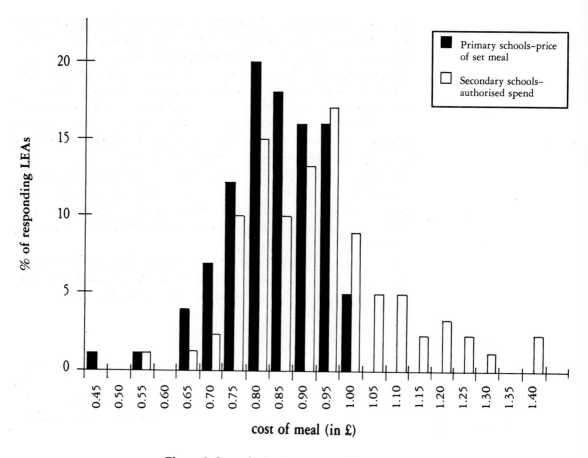

Figure 3 Cost of school meals in different Local Authorities

of soft drinks to sell to others would not normally be permitted! The authorised spend is usually more than the price of the primary meal.

Several LEAs mentioned that the price of set meals and cafeteria food would increase at the beginning of the summer term. A few other LEAs reported there would be changes in their contracts in April 1992. In interviews, caterers in particular, commented spontaneously that school meal numbers decline in the summer term.

It is generally agreed that when a price rise occurs, customers will be lost, but that most will *eventually* return. More than one price rise a year is not rare nowadays, particularly in LEAs where the school meals organisation anticipates a declining subsidy.

Provision for special dietary needs?

All but one authority provided meals for vegetarians, and all but two provided meals for children with health problems requiring medical diets.

All but nine LEAs made provision for the dietary requirements of religious minorities. Of those that did not, several indicated it was not necessary. Moslems are the religious group for whom special provision was made most frequently, followed by Hindus and Jews. The ethnic group most commonly mentioned was Asian.

Interviews with clients and caterers revealed that many authorities wanted to meet the needs of children of ethnic minorities. There had been efforts to employ Asian cooks and dining room assistants, and special items, such as samosas, had been bought despite the extra expense. One authority made efforts to develop recipes to help Afro-Caribbean children take pride in their inheritance.

In reality, children of ethnic minorities often enjoy British foods such as fishfingers, beans and chips, and show limited enthusiasm for special ethnic dishes. Some Asian parents advise their children to take easily identified 'safe' foods, rather than cooked dishes containing mixed ingredients.

Authorities varied in their attitudes to providing halal meat. The cost, training and reorganisation needed are quite considerable and only worthwhile if the schools can ensure sustained demand.

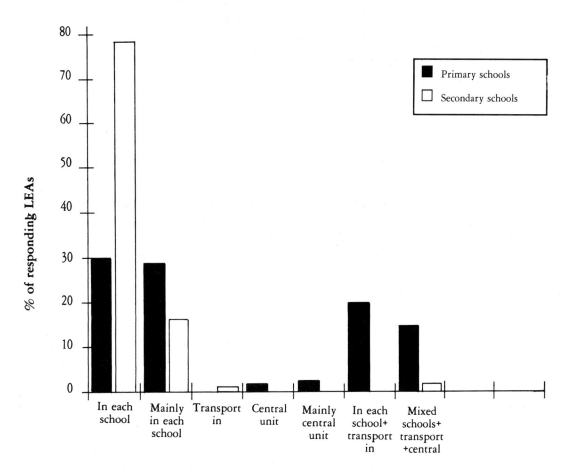

Figure 4 Place where food is cooked

Where food is cooked

Primary schools

Meals are prepared in all the primary schools in 30% of LEAs (Figure 4), and in almost 50%, most primary schools have meals cooked on the premises, with some transported in from other schools. Schools with 'transporting in' are usually those without dedicated kitchens or with small enrolments.

Few authorities made major use of central production kitchens, but around 15% used all three types of catering in their primary schools. Among our respondents, most transported meals were freshly cooked hot meals in insulated containers.

Comparatively little use was made of cook-chill and virtually none of cook-freeze techniques.

Secondary schools

In secondary schools cooking for the cafeteria-style menus is usually carried out in the schools' kitchens. 'Transported in' food is much less common than in primary schools.

Policies on food sold on school premises and where food is eaten

Food sold on school premises

LEAs were asked whether they had a policy on:

- tuckshops in school and what they can sell;
- vending machines and what is sold;
- vans inside school premises and what is sold;
- the age at which children can leave the school premises to buy a meal at lunchtime.

It appears from the questionnaire responses that over 60% of LEAs have no policies about either tuckshops (63%) or vending machines (67%) in schools. Only 20% had policies about tuckshops, and 16% about vending machines. In a further 12% headteachers determine the policies (Figure 5). In these authorities, with one exception which had LEA policies, headteachers also take responsibility for deciding whether vans selling food can come into schools. One-third (33%) of LEAs have policies about vans coming into schools.

The in-depth interviews indicated that if authorities or schools had no formal policy about, for example, vans on school premises, headteachers made decisions about what could and should be sold on school premises. In primary schools in particular, guidance was often given on what types of food could be brought into school by pupils to be eaten at break-times.

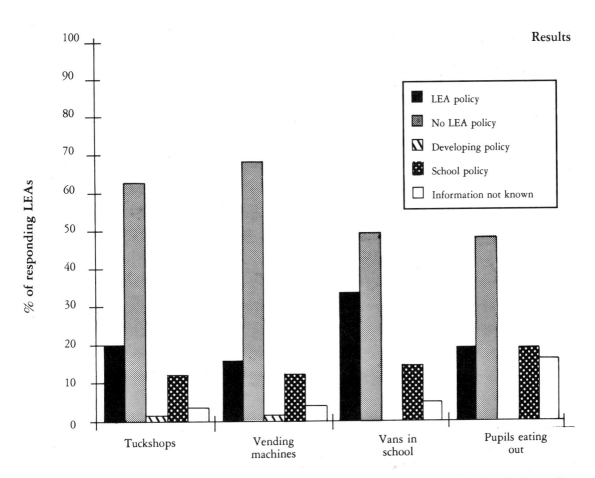

Figure 5 Policies about purchase of food other than school meals by pupils

Buying lunch off the school premises

From the questionnaire responses it appears that only 19% of LEAs have formal policies about the age at which pupils can leave the school premises to purchase a meal at lunchtime. In an equal number of cases headteachers determine the policy. It therefore appears that approximately 50% of authorities have no formal policies, but in view of the statutory responsibilities which schools have for children in their care, it would be most unlikely that such issues are not addressed by individual schools and headteachers. Evidence from visits to schools in the 12 LEAs studied in depth supported this view. All the schools visited had policies about pupils going out of school at lunchtime, including those in authorities where there was no formal policy.

CONTRACT SPECIFICATIONS FOR HEALTHY EATING AND NUTRITION

Of the 93 responding LEAs, all but two had specifications that included healthy eating. The two with no specifications both went out to private tender in the early 1980s.

LEAs were asked to send photocopies of the pages of their contract specifications that related to healthy eating and/or nutrition, and 58 responded. Additionally access was given to substantial extracts or complete copies of specifications, on visits to four authorities. Detailed analysis of the contract specifications forms Chapter 5 of this report.

Table 7 People responsible for drawing up specifications
(n=93, missing values=9)

	Number of LEAs (total responses=101, total respondents=84)
Client services officers	36
Client services (Education)	10
Education Department	14
Catering manager (Education) and school meals organisers	11
Catering advisers	6
Catering service	2
DSO	1
Competitive tendering team	7
Working group	2
Chief Executive's office	2
Local authority	2
Consultants	4
Health authority, dietitians	2
Schools	2

Who draws up the specifications?

Responsibility for drawing up contract specifications and evaluating tenders was (and is) with the client side of the school meals organisation. At the time the first contracts were being drawn up, catering was in the process of being reorganised into clients and contractors and its position in the educational structure was changing.

Table 8 Sources of nutritional advice for drawing up specifications
(Total LEAs=93, 2 did not know source, 24 did not report advice)

Adviser	Number of LEAs (total sources of advice= 111, total LEAs=67)
Dietitians including community dietitians	31
Health authority personnel (in general)	11
Other sections in own LEA	10
Consultants	7
Other local authorities	6
Education catering managers	6
Health education officers	4
Environmental health officers	4
Client services officers	4
Others	28

This reorganisation partly accounts for the rather confusing nomenclature used by respondents (Table 8). Where the health authority dietitians and schools were mentioned these were *in addition* to officers on the educational client side.

Sources of advice

Community dietitians were most commonly consulted when drawing up specifications related to healthy eating and/or nutrition. Next frequently mentioned were Health Authorities. In total, a wide range of health and nutrition experts was consulted, including the HEA and the London Food Commission. Advice was also sought from colleagues within the authority and in other local authorities, and from outside consultants (Table 8). Some authorities mentioned previous nutritional guidelines as well as, of course, the NACNE and COMA reports. Thirty LEAs used only one source of advice; the rest used several sources.

Monitoring methods

Almost all LEAs with nutritional specifications reported that these were monitored. One LEA was still developing its monitoring system; and two replied that nutritional specifications were only partly checked.

The most common method of monitoring nutritional specifications, mentioned by two-thirds of respondents was to check that the menus and foods on offer were as agreed in the contract.

In cash cafeterias, this often meant checking that the 'nutritionally sound' meal of the day was available. It was also common to check ingredients and bought-in products to see that they met nutritional requirements. One-quarter of respondents stated that portion sizes were checked by weighing. Fewer mentioned checking that standard recipes and cooking methods were being followed (Table 9).

Table 9 **Methods used for monitoring**
(n=93, no nutritional specifications=2, missing values=4)

Method	Number of LEAs (total responses 190, total respondents 87)
Check menus	37
Check ingredients	30
Check foods on offer	22
Check portion sizes	22
Check recipes used	15
Check cooking methods	8
Check product specifications	8
Nutrient analysis of sample meals	4
Others	44

The use of nutritional analysis was mentioned by 28% of respondents, but in only a very few cases did this mean that sample meals were analysed using laboratory techniques. More commonly, clients or contractors analysed proposed menus based on standard recipes using computer programs based on food tables. Thereafter only compliance with the menu would be checked. Similarly, suppliers would be asked to provide nutritional analyses for new products before they were adopted, but these were only occasionally checked in the laboratory.

Monitoring methods were explored in in-depth interviews, both on the telephone and face to face. Client officers reported that they checked the type and amount of food wasted when visiting schools. In addition they checked that 'healthy eating dishes', for example salads, were on the menu, but far less frequently checked how many portions of such items were served and chosen. Similarly by no means all officers checked that a healthy choice was still available towards the end of the serving period. Yet, apart from the nutritional implications, reduced choice towards the end of the meal break was known to be a common cause of student dissatisfaction.

During a monitoring visit, discussions were normally held with both the headteacher and the cook supervisor. Often both, but particularly the cook supervisor would be expected to sign a formal monitoring document. Client officers reported seeking the views of teachers and, slightly less frequently, talking with pupils. A few of the monitoring forms seen had space to record the pupils' opinions.

Monitoring practice

Personnel

Monitoring is normally carried out by client services officers, monitoring officers or their senior (catering) managers on the client side. Only one respondent mentioned the new quality assurance programme, but according to LACA (LACA, 1991) more than 40% of caterers are moving towards such programmes. In 11 LEAs the contractors were also involved in the monitoring process. Two local authorities reported involving headteachers, one used community dietitians and another mentioned that a nutritionist was employed as part of the client team.

Where an LEA's role has been reduced to the statutory provision of school meals, client officers continue to monitor the food provided to children entitled to a free meal. This may mean that the client officer retains a residual role providing advice to most of the caterers concerned. Much depends on the quality of the personal relationships involved.

Client services officers frequently have catering qualifications. The older staff usually formed part of the school meals organisation before CCT, and therefore have an 'inside' knowledge and understanding of the service.

Frequency

More than two-thirds of LEAs reported visiting schools on a regular basis, most commonly termly (Table 10). These visits might be organised according to an advance schedule. Alternatively the selection of schools to visit on a particular day, would be random.

Table 10 Frequency of monitoring checks
(n=93, missing value=1)

Frequency	Number of LEAs (total=92)
Each school annually	8
Each school twice a year	7
Each school termly	37
Each school twice a term	10
More frequently	3
'At random'	24
Other	3

The remaining LEAs mostly reported that they made random visits, but did not state their frequency. Over one-fifth specifically mentioned visits to follow up complaints.

Concerns

The in-depth interviews highlighted the following concerns about monitoring.

- **Most formal monitoring procedures concentrate on hygiene, health and safety, and the monitoring check lists observed on visits to LEAs usually contained very few questions on nutrition/healthy eating.** Officers reported that this was partly because of the inadequacy of specifications for nutrition. It also reflected the detailed, specific and enforceable requirements of health and safety legislation, which tend to assume priority.

It was reported during interviews that

- **Client officers might feel uncomfortable monitoring the work of former colleagues.** A particular difficulty was the imposition of defaults and penalties against in-house caterers in circumstances where there had been little competition for the tender. Some authorities viewed monitoring in a positive way as a means by which the client and catering sides could jointly improve the service. In one case caterer and client monitored together, in others problems were 'sorted out' informally by officers who had previously worked together. In some authorities the monitoring process was still evolving.

- **Time constraints and, in some cases reduced staff numbers, put constraints on monitoring.** Clients services officers typically have a range of duties, including responsibility for catering equipment as well as monitoring. At the time of the survey many officers were preoccupied with implementing the 1990 Food Safety Act. According to the LACA survey, in 63% of the 49 authorities responding there were more than 50 schools per monitoring officer and in 2 authorities there were over 300 schools schools per monitoring officer (LACA, 1991). Since only one formal monitoring – observing food preparation and serving – can be carried out in a day, some officers have been carrying out more limited spot-checks, perhaps when visiting the school or area for another purpose. Occasionally officers admitted that the monitoring frequencies given in their questionnaires were statements of intent rather than reality.

Penalties for failing to meet the contract specifications

The question 'What happens if contract specifications are not being met?' produced a range of answers.

- About 40% of respondents replied that there was a default or penalty system for fining caterers who failed to fulfil contractual obligations. Some indicated that the system would only be applied if faults persisted, and others indicated that the situation had not yet arisen.
- Almost 30% reported that shortcomings would be reported to the contractors, warnings issued and the contractor required to effect improvements, which the client would then check.
- Over 20% replied that they would hold meetings and discussions with the caterers and work together to achieve solutions.

The LGMB reported that 72% (16/22) LEAs had financial penalties (fixed level fines or sliding scale penalties) within their monitoring programmes (LGMB, 1991).

Difficulties ensuring that contract specifications are met

Authorities were asked to identify difficulties they were having and also to give details about problems they were encountering.

Less than 20% of local authorities reported having difficulties in meeting contract specifications for healthy eating (Table 11). This low response may reflect the permissive, rather than mandatory, character of many of the references to nutrition in contracts, or reluctance to admit difficulty.

Table 11 Difficulties ensuring that healthy eating specifications are met
(n=93, missing value=1)

Are there difficulties?	Number of LEAs (total=92)
No	67
Yes	16
Sometimes	2
Not yet	4
Don't know	1
Not applicable (no specifications)	2

Difficulties mentioned by a small number of authorities (total responses = 20, total respondents = 18) fall into five groups.

- Customer resistance to healthy eating, notably pupils at secondary level being 'addicted' to unhealthy foods (6 responses).
- Difficulties in monitoring and the need to close loopholes in specifications (5 responses).
- Difficulty catering for ethnic minorities within the terms of the specifications (3 responses).
- Specific difficulties with DSOs, for example poor paperwork hindering checking, cooks' lack of knowledge (3 responses).
- Financial implications, for example the cost implications sometimes involved in meeting healthy eating specifications and the high profit that can be made on chips (3 responses).

LEAs encountering difficulties in achieving specifications were investigated to determine whether theirs were particularly difficult to meet.

Of the 18 authorities reporting difficulties, 12 had provided extracts of their contracts with their responses to the questionnaire. These were examined in order to identify any elements that might be especially difficult to meet, compared with the others.

Of the 12 extracts checked, 4 LEAs had specifications that included mandatory elements for amounts of fat/sugar/salt/fibre in a school meal, or specified mandatory nutritional standards for macro- and micro-nutrients. However, 9 LEAs who did not express any difficulties meeting their healthy eating specifications, also had mandatory elements for the nutrient composition of the meal. The remaining 8 extracts did not contain any elements that were not

HEALTHY EATING GUIDELINES AND POLICIES

Guidelines and policies aimed at achieving good nutrition but not part of contract

Drawing up the guidelines/policy

common to other LEAs, who had not expressed difficulties regarding healthy eating.

Many LEAs reported having guidelines or policies on healthy eating, which, while not part of the contract, were used to promote good nutrition in the school meals service. Some had no guidelines. Others reported that their guidelines were fully incorporated into the contract itself. Altogether, 75% of responding LEAs provided information on their guidelines or policies in their responses to the questionnaire.

Like the specifications, the guidelines had usually been drawn up by the client side of the school meals organisation – by catering advisers, school meals managers and sometimes the Education Department in general. Most (71%) of the LEAs which provided information on their guidelines sought advice, usually from health professionals, but also from a wide range of other people or organisations, for example, other education departments, headteachers, school governors, the trade unions, social services and local councillors. Of these authorities 52% asked dietitians for advice, 36% consulted their local Health Authorities, and 10% referred to the NACNE and COMA reports.

Dietitians clearly play a prominent role in providing advice on nutritional specifications and guidelines for school meals. This aspect of their work requires an understanding of the realities of school meals provision as well as technical expertise, and this should be reflected in their community training.

Formal approval by the LEA

The great majority of guidelines and policies had been formally approved by the LEAs concerned. A few were still being considered and a few had not been officially adopted.

Promotion and encouragement

Information about how nutritional guidelines/healthy eating policies were promoted was provided by 70 respondents.

Twelve of those responding to the questionnaire reported that promoting nutritional guidelines or healthy eating policies were the responsibility of the contractor and not client services. Contractors who answered the questionnaire gave very specific information, confirming their involvement in promotion.

Quite a few respondents stated that promotional activities were collaborative, involving the contractors, the schools, and in seven cases, outside health professionals, both health promotion (5) and/or community dietitians (3).

The ways in which healthy eating is promoted falls into three broad categories (Table 12):

- advertising and marketing activities;
- promotion through the characteristics of the school meal itself;
- collaboration with teachers in nutrition education.

Table 12 Strategies to promote healthy eating

Activity	Number of LEAs (total responses=104, total respondents=70)
Marketing and promotional activities	37
Activities in schools	23
Approaches to parents	14
Informing the wider public	5
The school meal	29
Menus	15
Contract specifications (in general)	10
Recipes	6
Monitoring contract	4
'Traffic lights' selection systems	4
Nutrition education in schools	21
Collaboration with teachers in projects or in the regular curriculum	8
Other activities	15

More than 50% of respondents (37) reported that they, or their contractors, were engaged in promotional or marketing activities. Most of these were essentially school-based. Only 5 authorities mentioned promotion with the wider public. Typically, school-based promotions consist of theme days, healthy eating weeks or competitions for pupils. Twelve local authorities mentioned attempts to inform parents, for example by participating in parents' evenings (7 mentions), providing leaflets on the school meal, often with menus, or inviting parents to a school meal (mentioned once).

Several of the replies suggested that the emphasis was on promoting the school meal service, presumably as a means of promoting healthy eating.

Over 40% of respondents considered that healthy eating was promoted through the school meal itself, in particular through the menu, and the healthy eating choices it provided. The importance of the specifications, and the role of monitoring in achieving a nutritionally sound service, were stressed. Appropriately tested recipes and the need for ongoing training of catering staff were also mentioned. A 'traffic lights' or colour-coding system for promoting healthy choices in cafeterias was also reported.

Almost 33% of respondents mentioned the role of school staff in promoting healthy eating. Two LAs gave replies suggesting that most, or all, such promotion was left to teaching staff. Collaboration with teachers in projects, or in the regular curriculum, was mentioned by eight respondents, while two mentioned their own role in classroom teaching and two others were developing teaching packs. A few reported keeping headteachers involved and meetings of cooks, pupils and teachers within schools. Only one mentioned collaborating with the school nurse.

Table 13 Difficulties faced in promoting healthy eating guidelines

Difficulties faced	Number of LEAs (total responses=61, total respondents=44)
Customer resistance	16
Financial constraints	15
Need for school's support	13
Lack of time	8
Lack of materials, manpower and marketing skills	3
Other	4
Don't know – too soon to say	2

Note: Twenty-six respondents replied that they faced no difficulties. The question did not apply to the other authorities.

Customer resistance

The greatest perceived difficulty in promoting healthy eating guidelines is customers' unwillingness to eat healthy food (Table 13). Mention was made of the wide choice available at secondary cash cafeterias, of the discrepancy between teenagers' knowledge and practices, and the competing attraction of other outlets selling confectionery and 'fast foods'.

Financial constraints

There were several types of financial constraints, including:

* the general financial constraints facing the service, as reflected in the need for cost cutting and budgetary restraints;
* the contractor's need to make a profit, making it difficult to reject high-fat dairy products with EC subsidies and to risk losing customers by refusing to provide popular 'unhealthy' items;
* the lack of a separate allocation of funds for promotional activities.

School support

The need for support from within the school was seen as important, but not always easy to achieve. Generating support in individual schools was time-consuming. Headteachers were increasingly preoccupied; the demands of the school curriculum and LMS were mentioned. Some rejected the meal service, others installed tuckshops and vending machines to boost school income. All these actions frustrated caterers' attempts to foster healthy eating and decreased their profits.

Other difficulties

There were also reports of lack of time to engage in promotion, and lack of materials and skills for effective marketing.

Healthy eating and nutrition training for catering staff

Table 14 shows that 62% of LEAs had encouraged caterers to provide training in healthy eating and nutrition for their staff, and 44% reported that their caterers had provided such training in the previous year.

Table 14 LEA encouragement for training of catering staff
(n=93, missing values=6)

Policy	Number of LEAs (total=87)
Training encouraged	54
Training given	38
Training not given	10
Don't know if training given	6
Training not encouraged	30
Don't know whether training encouraged	3

A few of the 34% of LEAs who had not encouraged such training did not regard it as their responsibility to do so. There was a surprising number of 'don't knows'.

RECENT AND ANTICIPATED CHANGES

Starting dates for LMS

LMS has been phasing in since April 1990, though there were pilot schemes before this date. By April 1992, full delegation had taken place in 67% of LEAs (Table 15). The process will be complete by 1 April 1994, when the ex-ILEA boroughs, which have been on a delayed time schedule, complete implementation (Local Government Information Unit, personal communication).

Responsibility for catering under LMS

Only 7 LEAs reported that catering had become a school responsibility under LMS. In most of these cases the LEA's role in meal service had been severely reduced because of financial constraints.

Table 15 Starting dates for LMS
(n=93, missing values (no date given)=14)

Date	Number of LEAs (total=79)
1988	3
1989	8
1990	37
1991	20
1992	9
1993	2

Table 16 Will catering become a school responsibility under LMS?
(n=93, missing values=7)

Response	Number of LEAs (total=86)
No	23
Yes	4
Decision will be made at end of present contract	11
Not known at present, under review, don't know, maybe, under certain conditions only	41
It has already	7

Devolving responsibility for catering to schools

Most respondents were not certain whether or not responsibility for school meals would be devolved under LMS, some stating that the decision would be taken towards the end of the present catering contract. However, 27% stated that school meals would not become a responsibility under LMS in their authorities, compared with only 5% who said that it would (Table 16).

LEAs are not required to devolve budgets for school meals under the terms of LMS. Recognising the complexity of school catering, the DFE concedes that delegation should take place only if a school can provide a similar service at least as cheaply as the LEA (National Coordinating Committee on Competitive Tendering, 1990).

Where it is planned to devolve responsibility, the schools concerned have three options.

• They can stay within the central system 'buying back' into the LEA and asking it to continue to run the service, providing the client structure and arranging for a contractor through the CCT process as at present.

• They can 'contract out' and privatise their meal provision, using a private contractor, but not the DSO, on terms within their standing orders.

- They could theoretically set up a mini school based DSO, though it is very unlikely that schools could implement this option (NCCCT, 1990; Local Government Information Unit personal communication).

In-depth interviews revealed that the possible effects of LMS on school meals provision was not a present preoccupation for many LEAs. Some did not think that devolution was likely in their circumstances. Others felt that there would be time enough to face this problem when the requirements of the Health and Safety Act had been met since devolution could not take place anyway until the end of the current catering contract.

Attention was often concentrated on customer care to maintain meal numbers and on achieving greater efficiency overall. Generally strategies were being designed to put the service in a position to withstand a variety of possible future pressures, including reductions in subsidies as well as devolution under LMS.

One LEA was an exception. With its catering contract ending in 1993, a major initiative had been launched to inform schools of their options, with the result that the vast majority will probably opt to stay within the central system.

Problems

LEAs have identified a number of problems that arise if responsibility for the meal service is devolved under LMS. The following points were raised during in-depth interviews.

- The schools likely to want responsibility for their own school meals service are large secondary schools where cash cafeterias can be run at a profit, which might be shared between the school and the caterer. The schools that are likely to stay with the central system are small, rural and primary schools, which are unattractive to private caterers because meal provision is very expensive. Either the DSOs would provide a service to these schools at a heavy cost to the LEA or presumably the meal service would cease.
- Under present contracts catering equipment is generally the responsibility of the LEAs. In some cases this equipment is old and the LEA does not have adequate resources to replace it. The need for heavy capital expenditure in the near future might deter both schools and private caterers, depending on the size of the budget devolved.
- Most schools are unlikely to have the personnel to handle catering contracts or to monitor meal provision adequately. LEAs will need to define their own roles for schools with a devolved meal service. For example: Will school meals be required to meet LEA

specifications? Will caterers operate under LEA licence? What will be the monitoring role of the client services department? The suggestion has been made that schools might wish to 'buy back' into supervisory and monitoring services, which might continue to be provided by the LEA, even when the schools had chosen to use private caterers.

- Schools are unlikely to have the nutritional expertise required to ensure 'healthy eating'. Community dietitians are concerned about the amount of extra work that might arise if nutritional requirements have to be explained to individual schools. There would be a need to express nutritional standards in concrete terms of foods, portions and menu cycles, which could be readily checked by the schools themselves. The development of a computer package by the School Meals Assessment Project (see Note 2 on page 57) will help in this respect – as will the Berkshire healthy eating project 'The Eating Habit'.

- LEAs are worried about the effect of devolution on the continued existence of viable DSOs. In many authorities the school meals service provides employment to women, many of whom have family responsibilities. This welfare aspect of the service is particularly valued in some parts of the country.

- Attitudes to devolution are influenced by the fact that most of the LEAs where schools have assumed responsibility for school meals are LEAs that make statutory provision only. Devolution, *per se*, however, need not affect the subsidy, which would presumably be passed on to individual schools.

- Similarly, the examples quoted by LEAs are usually where private caterers have been unsuccessful in running a devolved meal service. Both ex-DSO groups and parents' cooperatives may lack management skills. Private contractors have only gradually gained expertise in school catering, which is different from other forms of catering in many ways.

HOW CAN THE HEALTH EDUCATION AUTHORITY HELP?

The questionnaire responses

Two-thirds of those answering the qeustionnaire replied to this question, and 87% of these thought that the HEA could help in improving the nutritional standards of the school meals service. The rest either stated that no help was needed, or were non-committal.

The overall impression is that the LEAs would like to be more active in encouraging healthy eating in schools and would welcome practical help from the HEA in a number of specific areas.

A number of the LEAs listed more than one way in which the HEA could help. Table 17 shows the breakdown of these suggestions, according to the number of responses.

Table 17 **How the HEA can help**
(Total number of suggestions=72; total number of LEAs making suggestions=53; total number of LEAs stating no help needed or giving a non-committal response=8; total number of LEAs responding=61; n=93, missing values=32)

Suggestion	Number of LEAs
Provision of specific information on the content of meals	20
Recipes, initiatives from other LEAs	11
Training courses, advice, information for different age groups	9
Support for national and local awareness campaigns	
Marketing, literature	17
Help in overcoming financial pressures	12
Advice about implementing nutritional standards within budgetary constraints	7
Providing funds for health promotion	5
Lobbying Government to reinstate nutritional guidelines for school meals	7
Encouraging parents to provide healthy diets at home	4
Providing nutrition education for home and school	7
Educate the children into adopting healthier eating habits at school	4
Help schools to incorporate a healthy eating policy into the curriculum	3
Other points mentioned by one or two LEAs	5

Not surprisingly, most requests, nearly 30%, concerned the provision of information on the content of meals in the form of recipes, advice, training courses, initiatives from other LEAs, and specific material on meals for various age groups.

Support for a National Awareness Campaign, which would help with marketing and literature was mentioned in just under a quarter of the responses.

Concern about finance was expressed in about 17% of the comments. The most common concerns were how best to implement nutritional standards with the current budgetary constraints and the finance required for health promotion. The caterers in particular were anxious for help on this subject.

Although only mentioned by two authorities, the request for the introduction of an easily used and accessible computer program to analyse the nutritional content of menus could have far-reaching implications.

In-depth interviews

In-depth exploration of ways in which the HEA could help was influenced by the use of an HEA checklist which listed specific suggestions.

The checklist was introduced by saying 'Other people have

suggested possible ways that the HEA might help. Are any of these likely to be useful to your LEA/ to your situation?

- Guidelines for running the service?
- Information/design of model specifications for contract?
- Information on foods and types of foods that would fulfil nutrient specifications?
- Help with menus?
- Help with healthy eating recipes?
- Information to use with the public/parents/teachers on the nutritional importance of the school meal?
- Retraining in healthy eating catering for caterers/cook supervisors?
- Specialist consultant advice?
- Workshops?
- Visits to look at examples of good practice – for whom?'

It should also be pointed out that while some LEAs were keenly interested in specific suggestions, others felt that these points were not applicable to their circumstances. For example, while some were interested in help to retrain caterers and cook supervisors, others had in-house training which they felt was adequate.

The three ideas from the checklist that gained the most positive response overall were:

- help with healthy eating recipes;
- information on the nutritional importance of the school meal to be used particularly for parents and headteachers;
- visits to look at examples of good practice in other authorities.

There was little difference in the responses from caterers and clients.

Further suggestions included the following, which are listed in order of frequency of response.

- Intensive promotion of the school meal service at national and local authority level, including pressure to ensure adequate funding (7).
- Promotion of nutrition education in schools/support initiatives/ development of teaching resources and materials (7).
- Provision of workshops on the implementation of policies on healthy eating in schools, for caterers and supervisors and in particular parents, governors and teachers (6).
- Raising headteachers' awareness of the service and its importance (2).

SUCCESSFUL INITIATIVES

In responding to the questionnaire, 31 LEAs described experiences they would like to pass on about successful initiatives for healthy eating in school catering. Many of the respondents listed such experiences in response to the question that asked how healthy eating guidelines and policies were promoted or encouraged.

There were four main categories of response.

- Marketing and promotional events.
- Menu choice.
- Parental involvement.
- Curriculum links.

Marketing and promotional events highlighting healthy eating, for example, videos, posters, and the involvement of local radio and television, as well as participation in national and local initiatives (Healthy Cities and Heartbeat Award) were mentioned by 12 LEAs.

Achieving healthy menu choices using various strategies, notably through menus and systems that colour code healthier choices, were mentioned by 10 LEAs.

The importance of informing and involving parents, for example in meal tastings, by providing menu leaflets, was raised by 8 LEAs.

Professional networks and support systems providing a range of expertise were emphasised by 7 LEAs. Strategies included multi-disciplinary working groups and contractors using community dietitians for particular processes, for example to facilitate menu planning and reassure parents.

Further experiences, reported by 7 LEAs, involved integration of school meals into the curriculum, for example by involvement of the school council and by applying healthy eating principles to vending machines and tuckshops. The importance of a whole school approach was stressed.

Individual authorities gave the following advice.

- 'Make food appeal to the age group you are trying to reach.'
- 'We have found that by offering a limited-choice menu in primary, where children are guided into healthy eating patterns, they make healthier choices in secondary schools.'
- 'We find it better not to advertise our meals as healthy – in many pupils' minds, healthy equals boring.'

During in-depth discussions three questions were asked:

- What advice would you offer to another LEA trying to establish healthy eating in schools?
- What do you think you have got right?
- What lessons have you learnt?

These questions were designed to explore more fully than was possible in the questionnaire the prerequisites for successfully developing healthy eating in schools. The responses were wide ranging.

Reflecting on their experiences, respondents stressed the importance of careful, strategic planning and moving realistically towards achievable targets. It was considered that an LEA food policy was helpful in this respect. Some felt that 'healthy eating' had been 'bounced on' people in the 1980s and, as a result, customers and staff had, on occasions, been antagonised.

Two authorities had made systematic use of 'roadshows', involving both senior client and catering officials, to consult with parents, governors and headteachers. They were not alone in stressing the importance of keeping lines of communication open.

Others stressed that children were the ultimate consumers. There was a need to understand and to be sensitive to their food habits. Imaginative approaches were needed for increasing choice, even with younger children, as well as recognition that tastes change as children grow older.

The application of modern management skills throughout the service was a prerequisite for success. Efficient use of information technology, including the use of computers to record stocks and sales, could facilitate continuous monitoring of progress and early identification of problems.

Two authorities believed that giving cook supervisors room for initiative was vital to ensure commitment to the service and the retention and recruitment of good staff. Others stressed the need for a defined career structure and the provision of training for staff at all levels.

Several authorities mentioned that they were developing teaching packs, linking the school meal to the curriculum. One advocated involving client services officers in classroom teaching on an occasional, but regular basis. One was developing a resource pack in connection with GCSE projects.

More detailed discussion of good ideas, including those observed on visits, has been included in Appendix 4.

5 CONTRACT SPECIFICATIONS: HEALTHY EATING AND NUTRITION

LEAs were asked to send photocopies of the pages of their contract specifications which related to healthy eating and/or nutrition. Sixty-two per cent responded and the extracts are analysed in this section. Additionally, during visits to authorities, access was provided to large extracts, or complete copies of specifications.

Contract documents range in size from a dozen or so pages, to 200–300. It is possible, and indeed likely, that authorities have requirements in terms of menu cycles, adherence to particular recipes and specifications related to ingredients and quantities that are not discussed in the photocopied extracts, but which *have* nutritional implications.

The question arises as to whether those who sent extracts of the specifications were typical of LEAs as a whole. It was possible that those providing photocopies had more adequate nutritional specifications than those who did not. Phone interviews were therefore held with a sample of LEAs who reported that their contracts contained specifications related to healthy eating, but who had not sent any photocopies. When asked about the nutritional components in their specifications, their replies suggested that their contracts were not very different from those of colleagues who had provided the additional information requested.

The summary analysis of the information sent is shown in Table 18 and background notes for this table are provided in Appendix 3.

A 'healthy eating policy' of some kind was included in 62% of documents sent. Sometimes this related only to the provision of school meals, sometimes it was a general LEA food policy, or part of a broader education policy. Only in 10% was implementation of a healthy eating policy mandatory. In such cases the contractor was required to 'adopt or implement' the policy, or it was specified that the contractor 'shall comply with the recommendations of NACNE/COMA'. It was not made clear by what criteria these requirements would be monitored.

A large number of authorities recognised the significance of the NACNE and COMA reports. They are mentioned, summarised, or form the basis of recommendations for 66% of the specification extracts sent in, but only 5% specified their implementation. One or

Table 18 Specifications for healthy eating in the contract

	Mentioned	Mandatory in some way	Mentioned %	Mandatory in some way %
Guidelines/policies				
Nutritional guidelines	26	8	45	14
Healthy eating policy	36	6	62	10
Healthy eating aims, objectives	15	1	26	2
NACNE/COMA	38	3	66	5
30% of RDA	7	5	12	9
Fat	44	13	76	22
Sugar	45	11	78	19
Salt	38	1	66	2
Fibre	42	11	72	19
Type of set meal	14	9	24	16
Type of cash cafeteria	11	7	19	12
Menus	26	7	45	12
Recipes	10	3	17	5
Frying	39	5	67	9
Size of portions	11	5	19	9
Foods to be served				
Fresh fruit	30	14	52	24
Yogurt	15	6	26	10
Salad	22	12	40	21
Types of foods to be served				
Vegetable oil	27	11	47	19
Wholemeal flour	35	14	60	24
Semi-skimmed milk	17	4	29	7
Brown rice/pasta	25	6	43	10
Wholemeal bread	20	9	35	16
Fresh vegetables	36	7	62	12
Nutritional specifications				
Energy	22	9	38	16
Carbohydrate	15	6	26	10
Protein	25	13	43	22
Vitamin C	19	7	33	12
Vitamin A	13	6	22	10
Vitamin D	17	5	29	9
Iron	19	8	33	14
Calcium	13	3	22	5
Additives	27	14	47	24

two authorities were careful to mention that these reports referred to the diet of adults, and noted that care should be taken when relating them to the dietary requirements of children. For example, it may be hard to provide younger pupils with adequate energy while maintaining a low fat intake, because of the bulk of starchy foods.

Of the documents examined 26% listed general (i.e. not related to specific foods) healthy eating aims and objectives and in only 2% were these objectives made mandatory by setting quantitative objectives, or a fixed time period by which they should be achieved. The types of objectives mentioned included:
• provision of education for staff and customers;
• provision and promotion of 'attractive, palatable healthy foods';
• the interpretation or formulation of dietary guidelines and specific recommendations for ways of achieving dietary goals.

One authority summarised the areas that its aims covered as 'nutrition, management, education and monitoring' and made detailed recommendations in each of these areas. Other authorities have a single, broad statement of intent, for example one authority aims 'to promote and increase the take-up of nutritionally balanced, high quality meals, with a bias towards encouraging a more healthy diet.'

THE NACNE NUTRIENTS

Many authorities are conscious of current healthy eating trends. Around 75% have included recommendations of some sort to decrease fat, sugar and salt intakes and to increase fibre intake. However, in very few cases are contractors required to adhere to nutritional standards, or to alter the balance of the diet in terms of fat, salt, sugar and fibre.

Most of the specification extracts examined contain recommendations regarding intakes: decrease fat (76%), decrease sugar (78%), decrease salt (66%) and increase fibre (72%). Some LEAs gave more detailed recommendations for achieving these aims, suggesting different cooking methods, recipe modifications, or the use of healthier types of commonly used foodstuffs. Many LEAs gave quantitative aims for the reduction of fat, sugar and salt, and increase of fibre.

One way in which some LEAs have tackled the problems associated with making such requirements mandatory (e.g. difficulty of monitoring, potential commercial non-viability) has been to stipulate that at least one meal (i.e. main course, carbohydrate/staple, vegetable, and dessert) from each menu must conform to the given nutritional standards and/or dietary profile for fat/sugar/fibre. It is not made clear in most cases whether the customer is informed as to which choices from the menu will form this 'balanced meal'.

Fat

Where quantititive aims were given for fat, it was usually suggested that 33–35% of energy should be derived from fat. It was also common for this recommendation to be associated with a directive to reduce saturated fat where possible. Figures in the range of 30–40% fat energy from saturated fat were usual when a quantitative recommendation was made.

Some LEAs gave qualitative recommendations for the reduction of fat content of school meals, for example:

- use of low-fat diary produce (many LEAs continue to use full fat cheddar cheese and whole milk, since this entitles them to the full EC subsidy on dairy products);
- reformulation of recipes to reduce fat content;
- use of cooking methods other than frying;
- ensuring no additional fat is used in cooking meat.

Although 76% of specification extracts contained recommendations to reduce fat content of meals, it was mandatory in only 22%.

Sugar

Decreasing the use of sugar was mentioned by 78% of LEAs and 19% stipulated that sugar *must* be reduced, giving either

- quantitative guidelines (i.e. total sugar content of school meal should not exceed 25 g; no more than 10% of energy to be provided by added sugar), or
- qualitative guidelines (i.e. confectionery must not be sold, the number of sugary desserts must be decreased).

When the recommendation was not mandatory, guidance for achieving the desired reduction ranged from the vague to the highly specific. For example, some LEAs suggested 'the addition of excess sugar to puddings and desserts is to be avoided'; 'limit added sugar'; 'sugar should be reduced where acceptable in terms of the end product'. Others suggested the use of low-sugar products, while some gave purely quantitative guidelines – usually that added sugars should contribute no more than 10% of energy. One LEA suggested that sugar should be decreased by 10%.

Opinions about the use of artificial sweeteners were divided. One LEA stated that sweetener should be used with sugar in a ratio of 9:1; others suggested that they may be useful for sweetening sauces or cooked fruit, and in low-sugar products such as drinks, and one LEA disapproved of their use. Most specifications, however, did not discuss the use of sweeteners.

Salt

Some reference to reducing salt intake was included in 66% of specifications. Generally it was recommended that salt in cooking should be minimised, and that the addition of salt at the table should be discouraged (e.g. by not placing salt cellars on tables). However, only one LEA made any of its guidelines mandatory. Many simply suggested that the use of salt should be 'limited', but gave no detail.

Fibre

A recommendation to increase fibre intakes was included in 72% of specifications, and the guidelines were mandatory in 19%.

Most LEAs who gave quantitative guidelines suggested a figure of 12 g per 1000 kcal (approximately 8 g per meal). However, one LEA suggested that the fibre content of a school meal should only be 4–5 g, apparently to prevent too great a reduction of the energy density of the meal.

Many LEAs also gave some qualitative guidelines, such as encouraging more frequent use of wholegrain pasta/rice, pulses, and the inclusion of wholemeal flour into baking. Advice given on ingredients to be used is discussed in more detail on pages 45–7.

TYPE OF SET MEAL OR CASH CAFETERIA

The type of set meal to be served was referred to in 24% of the specification extracts and in 16% of these the guidelines were mandatory.

The figures were slightly lower, but in similar proportions for cash cafeteria meals.

Guidelines generally related to the format of the meal (e.g. how many courses, how many choices of main course, vegetable, dessert should be available).

MENUS AND RECIPES

Menus

Menus, menu planning and structure were mentioned or sample or actual menus were given in 45% of the specifications. Less than 33% of these contained recommendations for menu planning that were in some way mandatory.

The most common type of reference to menus was a guide for the number of times a certain type of food (e.g. fresh meat, processed meat, salad, certain types of dessert) should appear within a designated period (e.g. a 20-day menu cycle).

A few authorities suggested the use of 'meal planning' systems, or coding for nutritional values as part of menu planning. One LEA stated that 'healthier items shall be highlighted'. Another LEA codes food by the Aquarian system (Finch, 1978), which is designed to help pupils select a balanced meal.

An alternative to this system is the 'traffic light' code system – high fat and/or sugar foods are coded red, orange indicates a food to be taken 'in moderation', and green indicates low fat, low sugar and high fibre foods, which should be taken freely. This method is mainly used in menu planning (i.e. by the catering staff), but is also provided at the point of sale in some schools.

Other systems used to produce balanced menus include a 'points' system, in which each dish is coded for fat and given a score. The total 'score' for a day's menu must not then exceed a specified limit.

The 'XYZ' system used in many ex-LEA schools is another menu-balancing system. Main courses coded X are high in fat, but desserts coded X are low in fat. Y foods – both main course and dessert – are 'moderate' in terms of fat and calories. Z main dishes are low in fat but

Z desserts are high in fat. Thus, no meal is very high or very low in fat if each course is selected from the same letter.

Recipes

Recipes were mentioned in 17% of the specification extracts, and some element relating to them was mandatory in 5%. Recipes were referred to in two main contexts.

- In some cases recommendations were made to revise recipes to decrease their sugar, fat, and salt content, or to increase their fibre content.
- In other cases, a 'standard recipe manual' was referred to, and it was generally mandatory that these recipes were followed.

METHOD OF COOKING

Frying was mentioned in 67% of the specifications (with some aspect of recommendations pertaining to it in 91% of cases). In virtually every instance this included a recommendation to reduce frying and use alternative cooking methods, such as oven baking or grilling.

Often more specific recommendations were made. Sometimes there was a list of the foods that were permitted to be fried. More often recommendations stipulated the number of times that chips (or other 'oiled' potatoes) could be served.

Chips

Usually the recommendation about chips was only applied in primary schools, or was greatly relaxed for secondary schools. Frequencies suggested varied from once a week maximum to at least one day a week without chips.

With secondary schools it was generally accepted that chips would be on the menu daily, but that an alternative (non-fried) potato should be available.

A few authorities specified that chips should be cut large and cooked rapidly at an appropriate temperature to minimise fat absorption.

Foods for frying

In several cases, a specified list of foods for frying was given. Only foods from this list could be fried. Those most commonly included were chips, fish, scotch eggs, doughnuts, spring rolls, and potato croquettes.

SIZE OF PORTIONS

Recommendations for portion sizes were included in 19% of specifications and approximately 50% were mandatory.

Generally where portion sizes were mentioned it was because a section of the specifications giving minimum portion sizes had been included.

Portion sizes were usually given for specific food items or dishes, but one LEA referred to the weight of the 'protein item' and 'full meal weight'.

One LEA made reference to healthy eating in relation to portion sizes by suggesting in its food policy, which was a non-contractual document, that there should be greater emphasis on large portions of starchy foods as part of the movement towards lower fat, higher fibre meals.

FOODS TO BE SERVED

Fresh fruit

Fresh fruit was mentioned as a food that should be served in 52% of the specifications and in just under 50% of these it was stipulated that it must be served at a certain frequency. Frequencies varied from daily (the majority) to weekly, though in some cases it was stated that fresh fruit or fruit tinned in natural juice should be served daily.

Some LEAs made other suggestions to increase the use of fruit, such as encouraging the provision of fruit-based desserts and fruit juice, and promoting the use of dried fruit as an alternative sweetening agent to sugar and as a source of fibre.

Yogurt

Yogurt was mentioned as a food that should be served in 26% of specifications, and was mandatory at a certain frequency in 10%.

Yogurt was often mentioned as one of a group of foods to be served as an alternative to the main dessert choice, especially for cash cafeterias.

One LEA suggested that 'yogurt and a biscuit, or milk drink and biscuit, or cheese and biscuit should be available daily' for its primary schools.

Yogurt seems to carry an association of 'healthy' food, because in some specifications other apparently unrelated foods became bracketed with it. For example, one LEA states that yogurt should be available daily in cash cafeterias, as must 'natural food products', though it does not specify what these should be.

Salad

Salad was included as a food that should be served in 40% of specifications and around 50% of these required that it be served at a particular frequency varying from daily to once a fortnight. Many also required that a 'salad' consisted of a minimum number of constituent items.

In one or two instances salads or raw vegetables, like yogurt, seemed to carry a connotation of health-food crankiness (e.g. one LEA stipulated that salad, raw vegetables, and 'wholemeal dishes' should be served daily).

One LEA recommended that 'popular' choice foods (presumably burgers, sausage rolls, etc.) should be served with a salad garnish to increase the uptake of salad and raw vegetables.

TYPES OF FOOD TO BE SERVED

Fats and oils

The use of vegetable oil was recommended by 47% of the specifications, but was mandatory in less than half of these.

Those not specifying vegetable oil were divided as to whether a certain type was required. Some stated 'good quality vegetable oil', whereas others specified vegetable oil, rich in polyunsaturates (and in one or two cases 'and/or monounsaturates').

One LEA specifies 'marine or vegetable-based fats'. A few mention that prolonged heating and frequent re-heating acts to saturate the polyunsaturated fatty acids, so a long-life oil should be used, and with care.

A few specifications recommended that any spreading fat (e.g. for sandwiches) should be rich in polyunsaturates.

Wholemeal flour

Wholemeal flour was mentioned as a commodity to be used in school meals catering in 60% of the specifications. In many cases it was referred to in the section dealing with ways to increase fibre, and was often covered by a general statement such as 'there should be wider use of wholemeal flour', or that a 'proportion of wholemeal flour should be used in pastry, scones, cakes, etc.'.

The use of wholemeal flour was mandatory in 24% of specifications, usually by stating a minimum percentage to be used with white flour. Percentages ranged from 15 to 33%. Some specifications also specified different ratios for different uses.

Semi-skimmed milk

A recommendation that reduced-fat milk be used for cooking and/or drinking was included in 29% of specifications, but only 7% had made this mandatory.

One LEA permitted only the use of whole milk, due to its EC subsidy. Another advocated using reduced-fat milk, except in nurseries, where whole milk should be provided. A handful suggested reduced-fat milk should be used in cooking, but that whole (possibly alongside semi-skimmed) should be available for drinking.

Brown rice

A recommendation to increase the use of brown rice or pasta was included in 43% of specifications, usually by a general statement suggesting that such items should be incorporated into the menu wherever possible, or used more widely. Inclusion was mandatory in only 10% of specifications.

One LEA recommended that brown rice should be used 50:50 with white rice; another that brown rice or pasta should be included in the menu at least once a week. Two LEAs stated that it should be used where possible, but pudding rice and canned pasta could be white.

Wholemeal bread

A recommendation to use wholemeal bread was included in 35% of specifications, and just over half of these authorities made its use mandatory.

Nine per cent of LEAs stated that wholemeal bread should be available 'in addition to white', one specified that a minimum of 50% of bread served should be wholemeal, and another how often it should be served.

One authority stated that wholemeal bread should be used 'in preference to white'.

Fresh vegetables

Of all foods in this section 'fresh vegetables' were the most commonly cited food to be incorporated into menus; 62% of specifications included some reference. Quite commonly fresh vegetables were grouped with frozen vegetables, and the two were distinguished from tinned vegetables. Ten per cent of specifications recommended that fresh or frozen vegetables should be used in preference to tinned.

Another common recommendation was to cook vegetables rapidly in minimal water and to keep holding times to a minimum to reduce nutritional losses.

Other foods

Various other foods were mentioned, but are not tabulated here. They included pulses, low-fat spread, low-fat meat products, low-sugar drinks and potatoes with skins.

Of these, pulses were most commonly mentioned, usually in a general statement recommending that they should be used more widely. Suggested use included adding to meat dishes to maintain an adequate level of protein while increasing fibre, and decreasing fat content; and adding to the range of vegetarian choices to reduce reliance on eggs and cheese.

Some specifications also recommended the use of fresh food in general. Sometimes this meant encouraging the use of 'fresh' as distinct from 'frozen' items. Sometimes it meant 'made on site' as distinct from using convenience products, such as sponge mixes or ready-made sponge bases. Some LEAs listed foods that could be ready processed, others did not seem concerned with this issue.

NUTRIENT SPECIFICATIONS

Nutritional guidelines were given by 45% of the LEAs, but were mandatory in only about 33% of these.

The detail given varied from minimal to highly specific quantitative recommendations for a range of nutrients. Some specifications simply stated that meals must meet the nutritional requirements of children, but 12% stated that meals must provide one third or 30% of the child's daily requirements.

When individual nutrients were mentioned, occasionally only energy and protein were considered. However, other LEAs listed the percentage of the daily requirement of energy that was to be provided by a variety of macro- and micro-nutrients.

Where LEAs did give detailed guidelines, the amounts specified are very consistent. This is probably because they are based on the CPG/BDA/London Food Commission standards described on pages 5–6.

Although the 'recommended daily allowances' (RDAs) published by the Government in 1979, have been superseded by new 'dietary reference values' (DRVs) (DoH, 1991), all the specifications examined refer to 'RDAs' because they were prepared before the DRVs came into use.

Energy/protein

Virtually all the LEAs who gave guidelines for nutritional standards included recommendations for energy and protein.

- **For energy, it was almost invariably that the school meal should provide 30% (or more) of a child's daily energy requirement.**
- For protein, most LEAs advised that it should provide around 11% of dietary energy, though there were slight variations (e.g. 'protein to provide 10–15% energy', 'minimum of one third RDA for protein to be provided by school lunch', etc.).

Guidelines for the energy content of meals were given by 38% of LEAs, and of these less than 50% were mandatory.

Protein guidelines were given by 43% of LEAs and just over 50% of these had mandatory guidelines.

Carbohydrate

A carbohydrate content for the school meal was recommended by 26% of the specifications seen and mandatory in 10%.

The CPG guidelines (see page 5) do not give specific recommendations for carbohydrate, but comment that as it is suggested that 11% energy is derived from protein and a maximum of 35% energy from fat, this will leave 54% of energy to be provided by carbohydrate.

Where recommendations for carbohydrate were included in specifications it was generally stated that a minimum of 50% of energy should be provided by carbohydrate. This was sometimes clarified by stating that not more than 10% of energy should be derived from added sugar.

Vitamins and minerals (Vitamins A, C, and D, calcium and iron)

Several specifications dealt solely with energy and/or protein, while most dealt with a wider range of nutrients, but omitted guidelines for one or more vitamins or minerals. Vitamins A and D, and calcium were omitted more frequently than Vitamin C and iron. None gave reasons for the inclusion or exclusion of specific nutrients. A small number of LEAs however did provide specifications for all the nutrients mentioned by the CPG.

ADDITIVES

A recommendation to limit the use of additives was included in 47% of specifications, either by keeping their use to an absolute minimum, or avoiding them, or excluding or reducing their use whenever possible.

More than 50% of the LEAs who made these recommendations, expressly prohibited the use of certain additives, most commonly E102 and E110. Some gave lengthy lists.

HEALTHY EATING AND NUTRITION AS PART OF CONTRACT SPECIFICATIONS

'All menus offered to customers . . . should incorporate the principles of healthy eating, after due regard is given to providing a commercially acceptable service.'

This quotation from contract specifications seems to summarise one of the main areas of difficulty that LEAs have when drawing up specifications for catering contracts. They feel an obligation to provide, and provide well, for the children in their area, and are aware of current thinking on the subject of healthy eating. In addition they perceive the practice of healthy eating to conflict with commercial interests – especially in cash cafeterias. As one caterer said: 'Secondary schoolchildren are less likely to stay in school if the food provided is not what they want to eat. This tends to be fast food, similar to that purchased from local shops.'

Some LEAs perceive provision of 'healthy food' only as an infringement of the customer's freedom of choice.

- '[The contractor should] ensure wholesome and nutritious dishes are available on the menu, while making sure that the customers have the right of free choice.'
- 'Customers should always be able to choose healthy food, but not be forced to eat a healthy diet.'

The fact that 'healthy' food may be perceived as a discrete entity, suggests that some of those designing contracts did not see healthy eating as eating a wide variety of foods with greater emphasis on some and less on others, but as a set of dishes, distinct from 'normal' foods.

LEAs also had to consider how to monitor the specifications for nutritional standards and healthy eating policies. Many LEAs' opening statements in the section of specifications related to food and health indicate that 'The contractor will support, as far as possible, recommendations made by COMA and NACNE.' Sometimes the wording is more directive – 'The contractor is required to adhere to the healthy eating policy (which follows the COMA/NACNE recommendations).'

It appears from the specifications seen that overall few LEAs make nutritional standards mandatory. One reason must be the great difficulty in enforcing such standards. Unlike hygiene standards, which are easy to monitor, confirming that a child's meal as eaten, contained 33% energy from fat, or 8 g fibre would be complex and time-consuming.

Surprisingly, many LEAs gave equal or greater weight to the reduction of additives and prohibition of some in school meals, than to the reduction of fat and sugar or increase in fibre. Yet the evidence suggesting that sugar intake is strongly associated with dental caries, and that high saturated fat intake is linked to heart disease, and low fibre intake to bowel disorders, is greater than the weight of evidence that suggests that some food additives are harmful to children.

Some LEAs have produced detailed specifications for menus, recipes and ingredients to help implement healthy eating policies but very few specifications extracts gave any practical recommendations as to how nutritional standards for specific nutrients should be achieved. Many also included notable statements of intent, for example:

- 'The school meals services should aim to market healthy food as the 'norm' not the exception';
- 'Every effort should be made to ensure that the meals most enjoyed and chosen most frequently by children are those which meet the nutritional specifications';
- 'The borough requires that the pricing policy does not [militate] against the selection of a healthier diet'.

Many LEAs were very aware that any efforts they made to provide healthier school meals needed to be done in conjunction with consumer education – by the caterer and within the school:

- 'The contractor . . . should endeavour to influence the customer, and where possible, educate about dietary matters';
- 'The Authority recognises the need to ensure that the messages pupils perceive are consistent, supporting and extending nutrition education in the classrom'.

In-depth telephone interviews were conducted with eight author-ities who had not returned contract specifications extracts, but who had stated in their response to the questionnaire that the contract did include specifications related to healthy eating/nutritional standards. These interviews did not reveal any particular differences between the specifications of those LEAs who had, and had not, sent specifications (i.e. virtually all mentioned NACNE/COMA and referred to healthy eating, but the degree of stringency for ingredients and nutrient composition of meals varied considerably).

Discussing contract specifications for healthy eating by telephone was difficult. It took some time, which many busy catering officers did not have, and really required that the interviewee had a copy of the specifications in front of them, which was not always possible. It was also difficult to find out in any great detail which ingredients and/or nutrients were specified and to what extent specifications were mandatory.

6 *VIEWS ON REINTRODUCING NUTRITIONAL STANDARDS*

During field visits the topic of reintroducing nutritional standards for school meals was broached. It appeared that many of those asked had not really thought about the possibility of government reintroducing nutritional standards, but there was a generally positive response. Seven of the twelve LEAs visited were in favour, though with qualifications, four were neutral and one was against.

There was a general feeling that central government guidance on nutrition would lend weight to LEA attempts to achieve healthy eating. Four LEAs stated that guidelines would have to be flexible. They thought that whatever changes happened in the future, they could no longer meet guidelines of the pre-1980 type.

Three LEAs said they would welcome such guidelines only if resources were available from central government (e.g. through increased subsidies, or by central government reinstating the old meals structure).

Three LEAs felt they would encounter no problems in meeting nutritional guidelines – at least in primary schools – because of their fresh-food policies.

A distinction was made between the application of guidelines in primary and secondary schools. In secondary schools it would be much harder and good presentation and marketing would be crucial to raise nutritional standards. One LEA described the changes needed in secondary schools as a 'quantum leap' and a 'challenge for the caterers'. Education about healthy choices would need to be much more linked to meal provision than at present.

Views about how the reintroduction of nutritional standards would affect labour costs for both the client and caterer and food costs varied, but doing so without the full EC subsidy would present real difficulties.

Any reintroduction of nutritional standards must take into account the need to maintain choice and variety to maintain pupil numbers, which would affect the price per meal, per child if they declined. Food wastage closely associated with the old standards was raised as an issue by all sections of the meals service, including cook supervisors.

It was pointed out that meeting mandatory nutritional standards could be difficult where a large number of products were 'bought in', with main items often in pastry or breadcrumbs, and where the school meals organisation had little influence on wholesalers. One LEA was concerned that private caterers might lose interest in tendering if such standards prevailed.

7 *ISSUES AND PERSPECTIVES*

A detailed analysis of suggestions made by respondents to the questionnaire and by clients, caterers and teachers during interviews about the help that the HEA could provide in promoting healthy eating is given on pages 34–6.

Suggestions made included the following:

- Provision of specific information/advice about meeting appropriate nutritional standards in meals.
- Support for school meals campaigns at national and local level.
- Support in overcoming perceived financial constraints.
- Reinstating nutritional guidelines for school meals.
- Support for nutrition education in schools and in the home.

It is recognised that the extent to which these suggestions can be implemented by the HEA will be influenced by national and local priorities. However successful support needs to recognise and to start from the felt needs of all those involved in school meals provision.

A number of issues that could be used as a basis for future discussion about school meals have been identified. Some have been identified in the past, particularly at the time of tendering by, for example, the unions involved and the Local Government Information Unit.

In reporting these findings attention has been drawn to the wide range of provision in the school meals service in Local Authorities. This service is influenced by the nature of LA structures, which in turn affect, for example:

- the nature of the contract;
- the client service arrangements;
- the terminology used in describing the service.

In planning for changes in the service it will be important to take account of these variations. Furthermore, before any changes to the school meals structure are made it is essential that all those involved, especially at LA level, define their aims and objectives for the service as a whole and acknowledge the different perspectives and points of view.

In considering the different elements of the service and how each contributes to the whole, it is evident that at LA level client and caterer may have different priorities. The division of the school meals service is relatively new. Clients and caterers are still defining their roles after the introduction of CCT. Inevitably in some cases there are tensions within the organisation and structure of the service. Currently many client officers are preoccupied with implementing the 1990 Food Safety Act, some in circumstances where the capital budget makes maintenance and up-grading of equipment difficult. The second round of CCT, allied to LMS, is likely to preoccupy Local Authorities in the medium term.

At present healthy eating is not a priority with the school meals organisation. Initiatives in healthy eating were carried out in many LEAs in the late 1980s. Major preoccupations now are efficient promotion of the service to sustain numbers and financial viability.

Changes in catering arrangements have been paralleled by changes in school management as schools work towards LMS. There have been major curriculum reforms as the National Curriculum is implemented. These have included new arrangements for national assessment of English, mathematics and science at both primary and secondary level. It is understandable that at a time of change school meals may not be a priority either in individual schools or the LEA as a whole.

School meals provision must be seen within the context of the school as a whole. Provision of meals is affected by the type and size of schools, the physical and educational environment, as well as by the curriculum.

Both teachers and caterers emphasise that in schools the theory and practice of healthy eating need to harmonise. If such collaboration is to succeed it must be planned and systematic.

Provision of school meals is complicated by the number of customers involved and their varied backgrounds. The pupil is the ultimate consumer, but the service has to be promoted to parents, headteachers, governors and the LEA. In this respect a school meals service is distinct from most other catering services.

Any attempt to reintroduce nutritional standards needs to be realistic. Food provided, but not eaten is of no use. Even in primary schools customer satisfaction is important. The trend towards providing greater choice, even for younger children, will make the provision of meals and menus conforming to particular nutritional standards more complex. In secondary schools cash cafeterias provide a challenge that has not been fully addressed by nutritionists.

Much is known about the food choices that children make. More needs to be known about why children make the choices they do. Without this knowledge changing food habits towards healthy eating will be an erratic and uncertain process. Short term and pilot promotions appear to have limited value in changing children's eating habits. Long term strategies based on measurable step-by-step implementation and agreed objectives are required.

In 1991 DRVs for energy and nutrients for the UK population were published (DoH, 1991), and superseded the 1979 RDAs. These provide an opportunity for LEAs to reconsider the nutritional aims and standards for their school meals. One LEA visited had already used its ongoing contacts with community dietitians to modify its requirements.

In designing specifications for future contracts, there needs to be a clear distinction between:

- intentions to pursue healthy eating ideals;
- nutritional requirements that the contractor is expected to meet.

A further distinction needs to be made between requirements expressed as nutritional standards, in other words levels of nutrients that must be achieved, and instructions to increase or decrease particular nutrients, the achievement of which can only be measured against a known baseline.

Effective monitoring is really only practicable where standards are expressed in quantitative terms.

For the sake of the school meals service and the relationship between client and cater, specifications need to be realistic and achievable, and the means of monitoring them clearly identified in the contract document.

REFERENCES AND FURTHER READING

REFERENCES

Assistant Masters and Mistresses Association and the Coronary Prevention Group. (1987) *Diet and disease: the case for school meals guidelines.* The Coronary Prevention Group, London.

Berger, N. (1990) *The school meals service from its beginnings to the present day.* Northcote House, London.

Burson-Marsteller. (1991) *What today's children are eating.* School Meals Survey for Gardner Merchant. Burson-Marsteller, London.

Child Poverty Action Group. (1988) *One good meal a day: the loss of free school meals.* Child Poverty Action Group, London.

Committee on Medical Aspects of Food Policy. (1984) *Diet and cardiovascular disease.* Reports on Health and Social Subjects, no. 8. HMSO, London.

Cragg, Ross and Dawson. (1991) *Guidelines for food policies at work.* Report on qualitative research prepared for the HEA. Cragg, Ross and Dawson, Ltd., London.

Department of Education and Science. (1965) *The nutritional standard of the school dinner.* Report of the Departmental Working Party on the nutritional standards of the school dinner and the type of meal. HMSO, London.

Department of Education and Science. (1975) *Nutrition in schools.* Report of the Working Party on the nutritional aspects of school meals. HMSO, London.

Department of Education and Science. (1986) *Curriculum matters 6: Health education from 5 to 16.* HMI Discussion Series. HMSO, London.

Department of Health. (1989), *The diets of British school children.* Committee on Medical Aspects of Food Policy report on health and social subjects, no. 36. Report by Subcommittee on Nutritional Surveillance. HMSO, London.

Department of Education and Science. (1992) *Statistics of education: schools 1991.* HMSO, London.

Department of Health. (1991) *Dietary reference values for food energy and nutrients for the United Kingdom.* Committee on Medical Aspects of Food Policy: report of the panel on dietary reference values. Report on health and social subjects, no. 41. HMSO, London.

Direct Services, Rochdale (1991). *Market research exercise on school meals.* Direct Services, Rochdale.

Education, Science and Arts Committee, The House of Commons. (1982) *School meals.* Seventh report from the Education, Science and Arts Committee session 1981–82. HMSO, London.

Evans, J. (1974) *Catering in schools and colleges.* Barrie and Jenkins, London.

Finch, I. (1978) 'The Aquarian system', *Nutrition and Food Science,* no. 51, March/April, pp. 2–5.

Fisher, P. (1987) 'History of school meals in Great Britain', *Nutrition and Health* vol. 4, pp. 189–94.

Food and Agriculture Organisation. (1965) *Food aid and education.* World Food Program Studies, no. 6. FAO, Rome.

GMB, NALGO, NUPE and TGWU. (1988) *Tender care, catering.* Joint union guidelines to compulsory tendering for local services. A supplement to *Who cares wins*. TGWU, London.

The health of the nation. (1991) A consultative document for health in England. HMSO, London.

Hurren, C. and Black, A. (eds.) (1991) *The food network: achieving a healthy diet by the year 2000*. Smith-Gordon, London.

Local Authority Caterers Association. (1991) *Education catering survey*. AVL Consultancy Ltd, Hanworth.

Local Government Management Board. (1991) *CCT information service survey report*, no. 4. Employment Surveys and Research Unit, London.

Local Government Training Board. (1990) *CCT information service survey report*, no. 1. Local Government Training Board and LACSAB, London.

Ministry of Health. (1945) *On the state of public health during six years of war*. Report of the Chief Medical Officer of Health 1939–45. HMSO, London.

Ministry of Health. (1973) *Report on school meals provision*. Ministry of Health, London.

National Advisory Council on Nutrition Education. (1983) *Proposals for nutritional guidelines for health education in Britain*. Health Education Council, London.

National Children's Home. (1991) *Poverty and nutrition survey*. National Children's Home, London.

National Curriculum Council. (1990) *Curriculum guidance 5: Health education*. NCC, York.

National Co-ordinating Committee on Competitive Tendering. (1990) *Compulsory competitive tendering and local management of schools*. Local Government Information Unit, London.

School Meals Campaign. (1992) *School meals take action*. School Meals Campaign, London.

Silverstone, R. (1990) *Healthy eating: a guide for chefs and caterers*. Macmillan, Basingstoke.

Spencer, D. (1982) 'School meals report turned down by DES', *Times Educational Supplement*, 12 November.

Turner, S. (1992) *Teaching and learning about food – a study of curriculum change in nutrition education in primary schools*. Ph.D. thesis. Institute of Education, University of London.

Wenlock, R. W., Disselduff, M. M., Skinner, R. K. and Knight, I. (1986) *The diets of British schoolchildren: preliminary report of a nutritional analysis of a nationwide dietary survey of British schoolchildren*. Department of Health and Social Security, London.

White, J., Cole-Hamilton, I. and Dibb, S. (1992) *The nutritional case for school meals*. School Meals Campaign, London.

World Health Organisation. (1990) *Diet, nutrition and the prevention of chronic diseases*. Report of a WHO study group. Technical report series 767. WHO, Geneva.

NOTES

1 **Data** The DFE collects data on the number of pupils taking school meals, the number of pupils bringing their own food and the number of pupils who have other arrangements. The DFE also collects data about fixed charges for school meals and the authorised spend for each pupil receiving a free meal in schools operating a cash cafeteria service.

LGMB surveys provide information about local government contracts including education and welfare catering contracts at six monthly intervals.

2 **The School Meals Assessment Project (SMAP)** is a computer-based nutritional assessment method for secondary school meals. Two versions will be available in

1992/93 – a monitoring pact for assessing a whole school menu and an educational pack for classroom use.

SMAP uses a week's meal menu and information about the types of ingredients and cooking methods used to show how the average meal on the menu compares with a recommended lunchtime amount for secondary school pupils. The recommended lunchtime amount is based on figures from the latest healthy eating advice – the COMA Report on Dietary Reference Values – and illustrates the content of the average meal for 12 nutrients including energy, fat, starch, protein and iron.

Modification to the menu or dishes can be tried out using the program. This is particularly useful when looking for practical ways to encourage children to gain their energy from starch foods instead of high fat, high sugar sources.

Information about SMAP can be obtained from Gill Cawdron, National Forum for Coronary Heart Disease Prevention, Hamilton House, Mabledon Place, London WC1H 9TX. It is funded by the British Heart Foundation and the HEA Look after your heart project.

APPENDIX 1   THE QUESTIONNAIRE

This questionnaire is part of a research project, undertaken on behalf of the Health Education Authority, which has been designed to find out the steps taken by Local Education Authorities to encourage healthy eating in schools.

The Health Education Authority is committed to promoting healthy eating in line with Government recommendations. In doing so, it recognises the importance of school meals in contributing to the current and future physical health of children and their ability to learn at school.

Many LEAs have gone a long way to providing children with healthy food choices at school; others may require further support and encouragement in doing so.

To assist this process, the HEA has commissioned the Institute of Education to carry out a review of the progress which has been made by LEAs to encourage healthy eating in schools and to explore ways in which support might be given to LEAs, caterers and individual schools. Identifying current positive initiatives will help others to make progress.

We at the Institute of Education should be very grateful if you could complete the questionnaire and return it to us in the enclosed, addressed envelope as soon as possible, posting it by February 20th at the latest.

We look forward to your collaboration in making this research and the resulting report really useful to LEAs in their promotion of healthy eating in schools.

All the information which you provide will be treated in confidence. We would however be grateful for the following details so that we can contact you if we have any queries:

Name of LEA ....

Your name, as the officer completing
  the questionnaire ....

Your phone number ....

Your position and department ....

If you lack the information to answer any of the questions, you may wish to refer to colleagues. If some of the questions do not seem to fit your particular circumstances, please write any explanations which you think are necessary. The right hand side of the questionnaire can be used to provide additional information.

Please do not hesitate to ring us if you have any queries about how to fill in the questionnaire. The phone number for the project is 071-612 6800. (Messages can also be left on 071-612 6776. Our Fax is 071-612 6792). Our address is Science Education, Institute of Education, 20 Bedford Way, London WC1H 0AL.

Thank you for your assistance,

Anne Coles, Sheila Turner
Project Directors

Please circle answers as appropriate

1 OVERVIEW OF THE SCHOOL MEALS SERVICE

The questions in this section are designed to provide us with the background information about your school meals service, which will be needed to facilitate analysis of the other data.

1.1 Who runs your schools meals catering services?
Direct Service Organisation? .... Outside contractor? ....
When did the contract start?   mth   .... yr ....
Length of initial contract?   mths   .... yrs ....
(If there is more than one contract, please provide information on each)

....
....
....

1.2 What is the annual value of the school meals catering contract?
£ ....
Is this the present price?   The tender price?   Don't know

1.3 What type of school meals service do you have? (If possible, indicate the number of schools with each type of service, or simply tick the boxes which are applicable.)

	Primary	Secondary
Set meal ☐		
Cafeteria style ☐		
Other (please specify)		

1.4 Approximately how many pupils use the school meals service each day?

	Primary	Secondary
Set meal		
Cafeteria style		
Other (please specify)		

1.5 Provision of free school meals.

	Primary	Secondary
How many children are entitled to them?		
How many eat them?		
Don't know ☐		

1.6 What is the price paid by a child for a set school meal?
Primary .... Don't know ....
Secondary .... Don't know ....

1.7 What is the 'authorised spend' for a free school meal in a self-service cafeteria?
Primary .... Don't know ....
Secondary .... Don't know ....

1.8 Is provision made for children with special dietary needs?
Vegetarians for reasons of choice   Yes No
Religious minorities   Yes No
Please specify which minority group ....
Children with health problems (eg allergies) Yes No
Other (please specify) ....

1.9 Where is the cooking mainly carried out?

	Primary	Secondary
In each school		
From another school and transported in		
From a central production kitchen		
Other (please specify)		

1.10 Does your LEA have a policy about:
tuckshops in schools and what they can sell?
Yes No Don't know
vending machines in schools & what is sold?
Yes No Don't know
vans inside school premises & what is sold?
Yes No Don't know
the age at which children can leave the school
premises to buy a meal at lunchtime?
Yes No Don't know

2 CONTRACT SPECIFICATIONS CONCERNED WITH HEALTHY EATING AND NUTRITION

2.1 Does your LEA have any specifications relating to healthy eating and/or nutrition as part of your school meals contract?
Yes No Don't know
(These specifications might, for example, relate to nutrients, types of foods, recipes or menus.) If yes, we would be grateful if you could enclose a photo-copy of the relevant pages of the contract specifications.

2.2 **If you have specifications (see 2.1)** Who was responsible for drawing these up? ....
don't know? ....
and from whom was advice sought?
....

2.3 Do you monitor that the specifications related to healthy eating and/or nutrition are being met?   Yes No Don't know

2.4 If yes, what methods of monitoring do you use
(a) with set meals, and
(b) in self-service cafeterias?
(For example do you carry out nutrient analysis of sample servings, do you check foods on offer or ingredients used?)
....
....

2.5 Who carries out the monitoring checks?
....

2.6 How frequently are monitoring checks made? (eg only when complaints are made, at random, each school termly, each school annually)
....

2.7 What happens if specifications are not being met?
....
....

2.8 Does your LEA face any particular difficulties in ensuring that contract specifications related to healthy eating are being met?
Yes No Don't know
If yes, please give details
....
....
....

3 HEALTHY EATING POLICIES OR GUIDELINES

3.1 Do you use guidelines or a policy on healthy eating which, while not part of the catering contract, are aimed at achieving good nutrition in school meals provision?
Yes No Don't know
If yes, we would be grateful if you could enclose a photocopy of the relevant pages of the document.

3.2 If you have guidelines, or a policy related to healthy eating, who was responsible for drawing these up? ....
and from whom was advice sought? ....
....

3.3 Have these guidelines and/or policy been formally approved by the LEA?
Yes No Don't know

3.4 How do you promote or encourage these guidelines and/or policy? (Please describe) ....
....
....

3.5 Do you face any particular difficulties in promoting these guidelines and/or policy?   Yes   No   Don't know
If yes, please describe
....
....

3.6 Has your LEA encouraged caterers to provide training in healthy eating and nutrition to their staff?
Yes   No   Don't know

3.7 If yes, has any such training been given in the last year?
Yes   No   Don't know

4   LOCAL MANAGEMENT OF SCHOOLS AND ITS EFFECT ON THE SCHOOL MEALS SERVICE

4.1 When did/will Local Management of Schools start in your LEA?
....

4.2 Has catering become a school responsibility under LMS? Please give details.
....
....

4.3 Will catering become a school responsibility under LMS? ....
....

5   HOW CAN THE HEALTH EDUCATION AUTHORITY HELP?

5.1 What help would you like in developing/maintaining/instigating the nutritional standards of the school meals service? (A selection of your ideas will be followed up.)
....
....
....
....

6   HAS YOUR LEA ANY EXPERIENCES IT WOULD LIKE TO PASS ON CONCERNING SUCCESSFUL INITIATIVES WITH REGARD TO HEALTHY EATING IN SCHOOL CATERING?

If, yes, please describe below or, if you would prefer, phone us.
....
....
....
....

APPENDIX 2   RESEARCH PROGRAMME TIMETABLE

JANUARY 1992

13 January — Contract awarded by HEA. Draft questionnaire produced in consultation with HEA and structured random sample of 12 LEAs piloted.

FEBRUARY 1992

3-7 February — Draft questionnaire revised and copied on gold paper, to make it more recognisable.

7 February — Pack mailed to 97 LEAs and marked for the personal attention of the Director of Education. It contained the questionnaire, letters from the HEA and from the Institute of Education, requesting it should be passed to the Client Services, or appropriate Officer, for completion and return by 20 February. Two self-addressed envelopes were enclosed for return of an acknowledgement slip and the questionnaire.

10-14 February — Field visits to 12 selected LEAs commenced. Card index system set up noting the date of receipt of acknowledgement slip and returned questionnaire. A tracking sheet was originated, 100 reproduced, each named and numbered according to the main education authorities directory.

14 February — Telephone calls begun to establish whether the questionnaire had been received by LEAs and note taken on tracking sheet of name of appropriate officer designated to complete. Calls continued until 95% of LEAs had been contacted by 21 February, the remainder by 28 February.
Questionnaires checked and specifications summarised on return.

21 February — Second sets of questionnaires sent out to those LEAs who had no record of receipt of first.

MARCH 1992

Field visits continued until end of the month.

3 March — First reminder letters sent, eventually to 23 LEAs.

16 March — Tabulation of figures begun on spreadsheets.

Analysis of tables and specification documents begun.

20 March	Continued follow-up phone calls until this date. Up to 5 calls made in some instances.
	Second reminder letters sent to 7 LEAs.
21 March	Formal telephone interviews arranged and carried out during last third of the month.
APRIL 1992	
30 March–3 April	Analysis of data from field visits and telephone interviews completed.
	Drafting of report begun.
3–10 April	Drafting of report.
10 April	Summary report presented to HEA.

APPENDIX 3 ANALYSIS OF CONTRACT SPECIFICATIONS
Notes on Table 18

Fifty-eight specifications were returned and tallied. This total excludes three that the project was asked to handle confidentially.

Guidelines/policies **Nutritional guidelines (mentioned)**
The specification included a section 'Details of nutritional guidelines' (e.g. aiming to meet 30% of a child's recommended daily intake), or more abstract statements, such as 'the contractor should provide meals of a nutritionally balanced composition', plus any appropriate explanation.

Nutritional guidelines (mandatory)
The specification included one or more quantitative nutritional requirements and/or stipulated that a nutritional analysis of all or part of the menu be provided.

Healthy eating policy (mentioned)
These specifications included, or referred to, a healthy eating policy. In some cases this was a general document (e.g. for the whole LA, or devised by the Health Authority for the district), and may not have formed a part of the specifications.

Healthy eating policy (mandatory)
The specifications included a directive that the contractor must conform to or implement the said policy.

Healthy eating aims and objectives (mentioned)
Specific aims or objectives for healthy eating were mentioned or listed (e.g. ensuring access to healthy food at affordable prices, staff training, education of customers and/or teachers. Specific aims for fat, sugar, salt, and fibre are included in 'Nutrients'.

Healthy eating aims and objective (mandatory)
This category includes specifications which laid down aims or objectives and gave quantitative and/or time-based limits for their realisation (e.g. aim to achieve x by y).

NACNE/COMA (mentioned)
These reports were mentioned in relation to nutritional guidelines or healthy eating policy for the catering service.

NACNE/COMA (mandatory)
The specification stipulated that the NACNE and/or COMA recommendations must be implemented.

30% of daily requirements (mentioned)
The specifications suggest the continued use of the 1975 DES-endorsed guidelines, and/or suggest a school meal should aim to provide one-third of a child's daily requirements (i.e. for all nutrients).

30% of daily requirements (mandatory)
The specifications require that the 1975 guidelines be adhered to and/or that a school meal must provide one-third of child's daily nutritional requirements.

Note: Nutritional guidelines and 30% of daily requirements may be expressed as providing x quantity of y meal, or to average out as x quantity of y per meal, over a period of time (e.g. 20-day menu cycle).

Nutrients

Fat/sugar/salt/fibre (mentioned)
The specifications mentioned one or more of these food groups as areas to cut down or increase. Quantitative or qualitative recommendations may or may not have been given.

Fat/sugar/salt/fibre (mandatory)
The specifications indicated that one or more of these food groups should be reduced or increased by a specific figure, and/or that qualitative (and measurable) changes should be made in the choice, preparation or cooking of foods which would affect intake of the said food.

Type of meal

Type of meal (mentioned)
A format for the meal was recommended. This could include number of courses, make-up of meal (e.g. main course + potato + vegetable + dessert), frequency of service for certain foods, etc.

Type of meal (mandatory)
A format for the meal was to be adhered to as described.

Menus and recipes

Menus (mentioned)
The specification included some recommendations for menu planning (e.g. frequency at which particular foods should be served in a menu cycle), and/or sample menus.

Menus (mandatory)
The specifications required that certain recommendations be followed when menu-planning (e.g. frequency of serving for certain foods, foods to be included in or excluded from the menu), and/or that menus be approved by the client and are only changed after permission sought and gained.

Recipes (mentioned)
The specifications included some recommendations for recipes to be used (e.g. ways in which they could be adapted, source of recipes).

Recipes (mandatory)
The specifications stipulated that recipes be taken from a certain source (e.g. catering service recipe manual), or be adapted in a particular way.

Method of cooking

Frying (mentioned)
The specifications make general or specific recommendations about the use of frying as a cooking method (e.g. aim to cut down on frying, use alternative cooking methods where possible).

Frying (mandatory)
The specifications stipulate that frying must be limited, e.g. to certain types of food and/or to a certain frequency. Instructions may apply to either or both primary and secondary schools.

Portion sizes

Portions (mentioned)
The specifications make recommendations regarding portion sizes.

Portions (mandatory)
The specifications detail required portion sizes, usually as minimum acceptable.

Foods to be served

Fresh fruit/yogurt/salad (mentioned)
The specifications encourage the serving of these foods. Frequency may or may not be mentioned, and the recommendations may apply to either or both primary and secondary schools.

Fresh fruit/yogurt/salad (mandatory)
The specifications stipulate that a particular food must be served at a certain frequency. This may apply to either or both primary and secondary schools.

Types of food to be served

Types of ingredients to be used (mentioned)
The specification recommends that these foods be incorporated into recipes, or their use increased.

Types of ingredients to be used (mandatory)
The specification requires that these foods be used to the exclusion of other types (e.g. semi-skimmed milk only), or be used in a certain proportion (e.g. 25% wholemeal flour), or at a certain frequency (e.g. fresh vegetables x times per week).

Nutritional specifications

Nutrients (mentioned)
The specifications include quantitative guidelines for the school meal's

contribution to a child's intake of the nutrient specified. Guidelines are given as aims or recommendations only.

Nutrients (mandatory)
The specifications give quantitative guidelines for individual nutrients which must be achieved. This may be per meal, or an average over a stated period (e.g. 20-day menu cycle).

Additives

Additives (mentioned)
The specifications include recommendations regarding the use of additivies (e.g. to be kept to a minimum, or aim to reduce where possible).

Additives (mandatory)
The specifications prohibit the use of one or more additives.

APPENDIX 4   PROMOTING HEALTHY EATING – IDEAS ABOUT GOOD PRACTICE

Examples of good practice identified by respondents to the survey questionnaire and during field visits by the researchers have been identified on pages 28–30 and 36–8. In this appendix some of these ideas are considered in more depth, and include suggestions made during in-depth interviews with client services officers and caterers and examples of good practice observed during visits to schools.

HOW TO ACHIEVE HEALTHY EATING

In many LAs there was a real and worthwhile attempt to introduce healthy eating in the mid to late 1980s. In the last few years, however, many LEAs and the school meals service have been preoccupied with other matters. In some cases LAs report that healthy eating principles that had been established are now being eroded as a result of financial cuts. It is essential that such erosion is halted.

While people are convinced that cash cafeterias in secondary schools are here to stay, individual schools in a few authorities have had some success with extended choice set-price meals provided through the cafeteria system.

Policies on healthy eating need to be agreed with schools. Such policies should include vending machines, the presence of sales vans inside school premises, as well as items sold at mid-morning break in tuckshops or snack bars. Caterers feel strongly that without such a policy, these alternative sources of food represent unfair competition and sabotage their efforts to provide healthy meals.

The food served

Fruit and vegetables

'Fruit is a dirty word and vegetables scarcely eaten in chip country.'

The sentiments expressed above are fortunately not universal. However, the promotion and presentation of fruit and vegetables as part of school meals needs to be thought through with care.

Small children can find fresh fruit difficult to eat. Good practices seen included making fresh fruit salad and serving half pieces of apple, orange or banana.

In cafeterias fruit remains unpopular. Changing its position on the counter may help. One cook supervisor placed the fruit bowl before the puddings. Another put the fruit bowl near the till and the check-out ladies encouraged those qualifying for a free meal to take fruit to make up their 'authorised spend'.

Salads can be tried to make up for a poor uptake of vegetables. Salad bars look smart but some children prefer to select individual salad items in bowls or paper cups. Allowing children to have salad with hot meat and potatoes if they wish is sensible.

Establishing close links with suppliers, including greengrocers, was seen as vital. Flexibility is required to enable schools to profit from low prices in times of glut. It would also seem sensible and this was seen in one authority visited, to provide small fruits such as kiwis, or small sized apples, which may be both cheaper and more acceptable than larger items.

Bread

High fibre bread or rolls can be made available as a filler, but in small portions to avoid wastage.

Wholemeal flour

The ability to introduce wholemeal flour into baked goods depended on the enthusiasm and skill of the cook and the success of his/her strategies, as well as the acceptability of the food offered. Surreptitious changes over time may well be the best method.

Promotion of healthy food items

Achieving nutritional change is not easy. The educator should start with the child's eating pattern and recognise that some habits are easier to change than others. Therefore where chips reign supreme and burgers are the second most popular choice, healthy eating strategies could be based on augmenting the nutritional value of the chips and burgers, for example by adding salad to the burger.

There are a number of ways in which healthy food items can be promoted, for example:

- ensure that healthy items are displayed attractively, given a prominent place on the servery and are well lit;
- provide reasonable quantities of healthy items as children seldom select the last item on a plate!
- use any colour coding system systematically and ensure that it is easily understood, with prominently displayed explanations and symbols, and that it is well produced and maintained in pristine condition;
- display prices and the menu clearly so that children can read them before they arrive at the servery.

Promotions are popular with caterers who feel that they serve to increase uptake of school meals. However, promotions, including 'theme days', often seem to be one-off events in specially congenial schools that have an interest in school meals and where teachers and caterers collaborate willingly. Where such collaboration occurs the events are popular, enjoyable and fun. These events are held in only a few schools, and are unlikely to make much impact in terms of healthy eating, but may encourage other schools in the area to participate in similar activities. The themes need to have direct links to healthy eating if they are to be of value.

One client officer pointed out that promotions are fine, but that there needs to be a long-term 'vision', with promotions forming part of a systematic approach to improving healthy eating.

It would be more equitable for promotions to take place *borough or countywide*, whether they are designed to be fun, to promote the educational value of food or to promote healthy eating. It is worth noting that much of the effort that goes into the conceptualisation and preparation of theme days at headquarters level would be the same whether few or many schools are concerned. Borough and county-wide promotions may require training of catering staff at school level.

The school meal is part of the total care package offered by primary schools in particular. Information about school meals can be used in school brochures to advertise the school's service.

Menu leaflets sent home to parents are a useful way of keeping parents informed. They can incorporate other information, for example, healthy eating guidelines or the dates of school holidays, on the back of the sheet. Where menus vary from school to school menus displayed near the school entrance allow parents to see what their children are being offered.

The suggestions made above are particularly relevant in the context of LMS. Everyone agrees on the aims of healthy eating. But with LMS it is going to be necessary to make it *easier* to get over the message and *easier* to provide appropriate meals.

Vegetarian provision and provision for religious groups

The range and variety of dishes provided is important. Many of the vegetarian dishes provided contain large amounts of cheese or are pastry based (i.e. high in fat). New recipes are needed to cater for the increased interest in vegetarian dishes. The new pulse recipes being developed by a few authorities are an excellent idea.

The initiative for the provision of halal meals should be taken by individual schools. Convincing parents that halal standards are being met should be the responsibility of the schools.

Recipes

There are some excellent recipe books, which have been adapted in the light of the NACNE and COMA reports and which have clearly taken much time and effort to produce. However, some authorities stated that they would welcome more recipe ideas. In view of the range of ideas observed the best solution would be for authorities to borrow or purchase some of these books of established and successful recipes.

Recipe competitions provide a means of maintaining and raising cook morale. Winning recipes can be incorporated into the recipe book used by the authority. Such recipes have the merit of being 'tried' – unlike recipes in books not specifically intended for schools.

Customer care

The school meal needs to be an occasion. The primary meal, as well as the secondary, needs to be *fashionable*. Unfortunately packed lunches with the sandwich boxes and their stickers and contents that can be exclaimed over and shared are often trendy.

One authority suggests that the youngest pupils need little rewards for clearing their plate. Nutritional standards are academic if the meal is not eaten.

Dining room supervisors and staff serving food need to be caring and sympathetic to the needs of the individual child and well versed in the principles of healthy eating.

Fresh and friendly uniforms for those serving food are important for both staff and children.

Leaflets suggesting parents' right of direct access to the school cook and client services officer through the provision of telephone numbers are a useful way of ensuring that children's needs are recognised.

The physical environment - dining rooms and serveries

The ambience of dining rooms in schools varies. Attractive posters, flowers or plants and carpeted areas were noted as ways in which dining areas were made more attractive. Two authorities commented that older children suggested adding plants and/or music as a way of improving their dining rooms.

A number of LEAs have invested money and effort in improving serveries. For example raised walkways in infant schools ensure that young children can see food and maintain eye contact with those serving it, which is reassuring for nervous or confused youngsters.

Those eating packed meals should eat in the dining room if practicable. This arrangement is less divisive and may result in greater uptake of school meals.

Food purchase

Pressure may have to be put on suppliers to produce 'bought in' items to LEA specifications. Where the marketing power of individual authorities is limited, collaboration with neighbouring authorities can be beneficial.

Vending machines, tuckshops and confectionery

Vending machines are increasingly common in schools. Products sold could be confined to healthier ones.

One LEA had initiated a healthy tuckshop policy, which others might be interested in adapting to their own circumstances.

It was observed that reducing the number of kinds of chocolate bars available for sale at any one time and thus limiting variation reduces demand in cash cafeterias.